SHERIDAN

The General Who Wasn't Afraid to Take a Chance

GENERAL PHIL SHERIDAN, the hero of Cedar Creek, barely met the height requirement for West Point cadets. There was also trouble at West Point over a charge with a bayonet, and he almost misspelled himself out of the Army before his career began. But, small in stature and short on formal schooling, Phil Sheridan—fortunately for the Union —was a big man in the ways that counted. He forced himself to study hard, and he learned, through bitter experience, to control his fiery Irish temper. He placed the good of his country and the welfare of his men ahead of his own personal safety, comfort, or reputation. Not only did he earn a place in the highest rank of America's military heroes, but also he heard the stirring sound of his own soldiers cheering, "Hurrah for little Phil!"

Colonel Red Reeder, one of the most versatile and gifted writers of books for boys, here for the first time turns his hand to biography, to tell the fascinating story of the brilliant and dashing cavalry leader of the Civil War.

Books by COLONEL RED REEDER

WEST POINT PLEBE

WEST POINT YEARLING

WEST POINT SECOND CLASSMAN

WEST POINT FIRST CLASSMAN

2ND LIEUTENANT CLINT LANE: WEST POINT TO BERLIN

CLINT LANE IN KOREA

ATTACK AT FORT LOOKOUT

WHISPERING WIND

THE SHERIFF OF HAT CREEK

THE MACKENZIE RAID

THE STORY OF THE CIVIL WAR

THE STORY OF THE REVOLUTIONARY WAR

THE STORY OF THE WAR OF 1812

POINTERS ON ATHLETICS

SHERIDAN: THE GENERAL WHO WASN'T AFRAID TO TAKE A CHANCE

With *NARDI REEDER CAMPION*

THE WEST POINT STORY

SHERIDAN

The General Who Wasn't Afraid to Take a Chance

BY
COLONEL RED REEDER

DUELL, SLOAN AND PEARCE

New York

B
Sheridan
Reeder

Affiliate of
MEREDITH PRESS
Des Moines & New York

Manufactured in the United States of America for Meredith Press

VAN REES PRESS • NEW YORK

To

HARRY PURNELL STORKE

Lieutenant General, United States Army

Author's Note

My wife, Dort Darrah Reeder, is improving as a counselor, stenographer, typist, editor, and copy reader. Without her advice on the story and the English language, including its punctuation and allied mysteries, this author would be baffled.

My sister, Nardi Reeder Campion, gave me advice about the early stages of this book which caused me to tear up several chapters. I also appreciate *her* help.

I am indebted to Dr. Ted Speers, Miss Thelma Bedell, Ken Rapp, Floyd S. Nelson, Lieutenant Colonel John Elting, Al Murphy, Master Sergeant Paul La Casse, Major General Scott Riggs, U.S.A., retired, and the staff at the Library of Congress and at the National Archives. The members of the staff of the U.S.M.A. Library at West Point are helpful, patient, and interested. I must thank Living History, Inc., republishers of *Harper's Weekly*.

I am obligated also to The Massachusetts Historical Society for use of a quote from Colonel Theodore Lyman of the Union Army.

RED REEDER

West Point,
New York

DEPARTMENT OF MILITARY ART AND ENGINEERING
UNITED STATES MILITARY ACADEMY

WEST POINT, NEW YORK

FOREWORD

The story of Philip Henry Sheridan, which Colonel Red
Reeder tells here in his usual inimitably vivid way, is
one that every American boy should seriously consider.
Sheridan's parents were relatively poor, yet
Phil Sheridan, through years of study, hard work, and
danger, finally became the Commanding General of the
United States Army. Born with a furious temper, he
learned to keep it under iron self-control. As brave
and dashing a cavalry leader as J. E. B. Stuart or
Nathan Bedford Forrest, Sheridan also knew that the
successful general must make certain that his men are as
well equipped and fed as possible. Throughout his career,
he was always willing to fight -- and also to study.
He constantly sought new and better ways of carrying
out his duties as an officer of the United States Army.
"Whatever I took up," he once said, "even if it were the
simplest of duties, I tried to do it better than it had
ever been done before."
The history of Sheridan's life is another example of
what one American boy was able to accomplish, largely
through his own efforts. He served the United States
loyally and energetically all his life, and his place
amongst our military heroes was honestly earned.

VINCENT J. ESPOSITO, Col.
Professor of Military History
United States Military Academy

Contents

1. THE BROWN ENVELOPE   3
2. THE NEW WORLD   10
3. HALT! WHO GOES THERE?   18
4. THE PLAQUE WITHOUT A NAME   32
5. FIX BAYONETS!   39
6. THE BIG QUESTION   50
7. INDIAN COUNTRY—TEXAS   61
8. TRIP TO OREGON   71
9. INDIAN COUNTRY—OREGON   79
10. "I WILL NOT GIVE UP THIS FORT"   88
11. "ALL I WANT IS A CHANCE"   100
12. THE BATTLE OF PERRYVILLE   113
13. THE BATTLE OF STONES RIVER   125
14. JIM CARD—SPY   140
15. DEFEAT AT CHICKAMAUGA; OUT OF THE TRAP AT MISSIONARY RIDGE   154
16. THE SNAPPING TURTLE   165

Contents

17. RAID AT YELLOW TAVERN   178

18. "TOO YOUNG FOR THE JOB"   186

19. INTO THE VALLEY   197

20. PHIL SHERIDAN AT CEDAR CREEK   210

21. PHIL HELPS TO END THE WAR   220

    FOR FURTHER READING   231

    SELECTED BOOKS   233

    INDEX   235

Illustrations

following page 82

View of West Point

Lieutenant George W. Crook, Cadet Phil Sheridan, and
Lieutenant John Nugent

Lost Dispatches

The Patient Pack-mule

Mounted Indian

The Bombardment of Sumter

The First Virginia Cavalry

Lincoln Reviewing the Cavalry of the Army of the Potomac

Sheridan and His Staff

Attack on Union Supply Train

Battle of Chickamauga

The Courier

Sheridan's Wagon Trains

Hospital Attendants Collecting the Wounded

Railroad Bridge over the North Anna

Captured by Mosby's Guerrillas

Colonel John S. Mosby

7th New York Heavy Artillery at Cold Harbor

Pontoon Bridge on the James River

General Lee after the Surrender

MAPS

Northwest   93

Stones River   132

Chickamauga   152

Cold Harbor   191

Shenandoah Valley   199

SHERIDAN

The General Who Wasn't Afraid to Take a Chance

"The people I want to hear about are the people who take risks."

—ROBERT FROST

CHAPTER 1

The Brown Envelope

P<small>HIL</small> S<small>HERIDAN</small> told his mother and father at breakfast that this was the day he would ask Mr. McNanly the big question.

"You'll get an honest answer," Mr. Sheridan said. "I don't know anybody better." Phil's father poured his coffee into his saucer, blew on it, and drank. It sounded like water gurgling down a pipe. Mr. Sheridan folded his newspaper and Phil glimpsed the headlines.

PRESIDENT SAYS SCOTT TO LAND VERA CRUZ, MARCH 1847

"President Polk knows what he's doing, sending General Scott," Mr. Sheridan said. "Things'll pop next spring in Mexico." He looked at the clock on the mantel, stood up, and wiped his mouth on his sleeve.

At the door he turned. "I'm glad you're askin' Mr. McNanly," he said to Phil. "I tell ye this, don't be a contractor when ye grow up. Run a man crazy. Right now, every time we finish a new stretch of macadam, the pioneers headin' west want to drive over it afore it's cooled."

Mrs. Sheridan placed a helping of scrambled eggs on Phil's plate, but he was too worried to eat. His mind was on his coming talk with the teacher. That talk meant everything.

The brisk December air was the bracer Phil Sheridan needed. On the walk along the dirt road to school children called to him, but he barely heard. He rehearsed his talk with Mr. McNanly, the principal—the wisest man in Somerset, Ohio. Phil prayed silently.

But things did not go smoothly. Mr. McNanly brought two of the biggest boys in front of the school and put a birch rod to them. Their crime was playing hooky. This added to Phil's nervousness. He had played hooky last week. The only good thing about the "whipping day," as Mr. McNanly called it, was that it took up most of the spelling period. Phil hated spelling.

Phil Sheridan was hesitant about questioning the teacher because the fewer relations he had with the fiery man the better. There was also fear in Philip that the teacher might say no. But his parents insisted it was the thing to do. Phil tightened his belt.

When school was over and the room quiet, Phil stood before the principal's desk and explained his dream. Phil talked faster than ever. He rattled off unplanned sentences. Mr. McNanly peered through his spectacles as he listened, his neck craned forward like a turtle's.

Phil finished, "And, sir, if I study hard—harder—do you think I can pass the examinations for West Point? I want to be a West Point cadet."

Phil held his breath. He felt the teacher would never reply.

Finally, Mr. McNanly said, "Maybe ye belong in the Army. Ye've fought every bye in school. Ye have the devil's own temper. When are ye going to bridle it?"

It was a startling question. Phil knew he had a reputation for a temper, but Mr. McNanly had the worst temper in town.

Mr. McNanly said, "Let's figure it out. In two years ye'll be seventeen. Taking the exams this minute ye wouldn't have a ghost of a show. Ye can't even spell 'cat.' Better marks, too, in math, I want to see. Seize these two years and work. Prepare yourself for West Point and the examinations. West Point is a challenge. Tell me again, and not so fast, why you want to go to the Academy."

"I'd like an officer's life, sir. It's outdoors with men— all over the country."

"It's not an easy life, and it could take a turn for the harder. Ye take—well, the Union's not thinking together. Slavery is a red-hot iron of a question. I think ye'd make a fair Army officer, but your studies—your spelling is atrocious. How do ye spell 'atrocious'?"

"A-t-t—"

"No, no. If ye don't spell better than that two years from now, the professors up at the Academy will faint when they read your English exam. But what about Patrick? He's the scholar. Once your father said Patrick would be the West Point cadet from the Sheridans."

"Patrick told us after Mass last Sunday that he does not want to go to West Point."

"Well, my answer is, 'Ye can make it if ye work.' I'm

not talkin' about work like you do at Fink and Dittoe's. In the store ye do well. It's studying, I mean."

"Thank you, sir." Phil felt as if a load had been lifted from his back. Then he asked another question that weighted his mind. "Sir, do you think I'm tall enough to be a cadet?"

Mr. McNanly stood up, the better to gauge Phil's lack of height. "How tall are ye?"

"Five feet five, sir?"

Phil trembled while the teacher sized him up.

"Ye'll probably grow."

Phil rushed home to tell his mother about the interview. He began to read everything he could about West Point. He discovered that the upperclassmen hazed the new cadets more than freshmen were hazed in civilian colleges. He talked to his mother about this.

"Congress," Mrs. Sheridan said, "is trying to stop it, but I cannot see it bothering an Irishman."

Phil had another worry. He discovered that candidates for the Military Academy had to travel all the way to West Point, New York, to take the entrance examinations. "Supposing I go all that distance," he asked his mother, "and fail?"

His mother smiled her wonderful smile. " 'Tis all right you're going to be. You are studying. Now, my good boy, you first have to pass your term examinations right here in Somerset. Worry about them. I learned long ago, 'Life is hard by the yard but a cinch by the inch.' "

Phil wrote Congressman Thomas Ritchey of Ohio asking for an appointment to West Point. That letter bore no misspelled words.

A month crawled by. When each mail arrived Phil

haunted the post office. He didn't receive even an advertisement.

About the time he figured that the Congressman would not answer, the postmaster handed Phil a letter. The envelope was marked OFFICIAL BUSINESS, THE HOUSE OF REPRESENTATIVES. THE CONGRESS OF THE UNITED STATES. WASHINGTON CITY, D. C. Phil trembled. He tore open the envelope. The letter read:

Dear Philip Sheridan,

I am pleased to appoint you to the United States Military Academy as a first alternate from our District. *If* the principal fails, the appointment is yours.

In answer to your question, I think you are tall enough to become a cadet.

Phil's face fell. It was hard to conceal his disappointment. "I'll never get there," he told his mother. "That other boy will pass. I'm a second fiddle. What shall I do? He doesn't even know if I'm tall enough."

"You must never give up," his mother said. "Study harder. You must act as if you had the real appointment."

Phil believed his chances were slim, but he kept on studying. It was harder to concentrate now. Every day he wondered what "that other boy" was doing.

When he was in Mr. Dittoe's store one day, working on the accounts, a farmer came in and announced he had his wagon loaded with hundred-pound sacks of cornmeal. He said he wanted to trade some of it for a tea-kettle, a pair of fur gloves, four woolen blankets, a Mackinaw, and a dozen large needles. It was Phil's job to determine how much cornmeal the farmer would have to trade Mr. Dittoe for the merchandise.

Mr. Dittoe entered the store and looked over Phil's shoulder. "Phil," he said, "I'll take over. There's an official business envelope at the post office waiting for you."

Phil sprinted down the street. It was hard to breathe, he was so excited. The brown envelope bore the heading, THE ADJUTANT GENERAL, U. S. ARMY, WAR DE-PARTMENT, WASHINGTON CITY, D. C. The first part of the letter was hard to understand. The letter went on: *Therefore, Mr. Sheridan, you are appointed as a candidate to the United States Military Academy, subject to your passing the required mental and physical examinations. You will report to the Adjutant, West Point, N. Y., June 28, 1848 to be examined.*

Phil read and reread the letter. He wanted to be sure he understood what it said. He showed it to the postmaster as a check. "That's right," the postmaster said. "Marvelous. The other boy quit. All you have to do is go to West Point and pass and you're in. Congratulations."

Phil's heart leaped. *All I have to do is pass,* he thought, *but can I pass?*

He streaked for home and threw himself in his mother's arms. "Didn't I tell you," she said, "they can't beat the Irish?"

A week later Phil stood in front of Finch's tavern with his father, waiting for the stagecoach. Two Negro boys played marbles in the dirt road. Phil wore his brown broadcloth suit. It itched. The stage was late, and Phil decided it would never come. The man and boy did not talk. It was an awkward time. Suddenly the boy realized how much he loved his father.

Mr. Sheridan placed his arm across Phil's sturdy shoulders. "Philip, this is your big chance. I hope ye have luck. I never went far in school."

A Negro boy in the road leaped up. "Here come de stagecoach!" he shouted.

The coach dashed down the main street, shrouded with dust. The brakes screeched as the driver yelled, "Whoa!" He reined in the horses. Quickly, stableboys unharnessed the four tired animals. Fresh ones were trotted out. The driver called to a stable hand, "That off forewheel needs grease."

Philip paid his fare to the driver and tossed his carpetbag aboard. He kissed his father good-bye, and, in a moment, the coach raced out of town headed for Zanesville, Ohio.

When the stagecoach was a half-mile out of Somerset, the driver pulled his horses to a walk and kept them there until they reached the outskirts of Zanesville. Then he whipped them into a gallop.

The driver would not let Phil sit beside him on the box, so Phil curled up in a corner of the back seat with a sack of mail. He felt lonely, but he was glad to be aboard.

Phil Sheridan, the boy who would become the youngest of the four greatest Union commanders and one of the most dashing battlefield leaders in history, was on his way.

CHAPTER 2

The New World

PHIL felt as if the stagecoach were taking him to the end of the world. He already missed his mother, brothers, and sisters.

The road was rough most of the way. In Zanesville he climbed aboard a barge on the Ohio and Erie Canal and paid his fare to Cleveland. The barge slipped along noiselessly except for the occasional curse of the mule driver on the bank. The driver seemed to think his oaths inspired the four mules towing the barge.

In many of the fields men worked to pull out tree stumps with oxen. Phil took his spelling book from his carpetbag, but it was hard to study. The countryside was too fascinating. And, sitting with the captain on top of the forward cabin, was an interesting-looking man. He had the shoulders of a boxer. He wore a large hat, a clawhammer coat, and trousers thrust into knee-high boots. From his belt hung a pair of handcuffs and a horse pistol in a leather holster.

A Negro boat hand volunteered to Phil, "Dat man is a

pro-fessional slave-catcher. I'm glad I'm a free man in a free state. Dat man gits two dollars a day irregardless of whether he catches de runaway nigger or not. If he catches him he gits a bonus. He told de cap'n dat Cleveland's a depot on de Underground Railroad, and dat he gwine to nestle down and lay for de man he's after. 'Course, de Underground Railroad ain't a sure 'nuff railroad. It's just a sayin'. I knew a white man who worked in Cleveland helpin' on the U.G., but they locked him up for bein' a black-hearted abolisher."

"You mean abolitionist?" asked Phil.

"Dat's what I said, abolisher."

"Why did they lock him up?"

"Just 'cause dey didn't like the way he talked. He told everybody, 'The gov'mint recognizes slavery, so let's git rid o' de gov'mint.' So dey jailed him. Den dey bailed him out. You want to see for yourself, go to South Ohio."

The slave-catcher offered the captain a cigar and lit one for himself. The boat hand said to Phil with awe, "He smokes as many as seven a day. He's big-rich."

Phil wished his brothers and sisters could see the slave-catcher.

Phil placed the red spelling book back in his bag. The sun was too bright, anyhow. It made the pages glisten.

At the Cleveland docks the crowds of people made Phil think of flies on honey. Steamers were lined up, their ornamented pilot houses looking like imposing dwellings. Black smoke poured upward. The docks were littered with boxes, casks, wagons, plows, sacks of grain, and piles of lumber. Drays rattled about the docks, bringing more supplies. Every once in a while a steamer snorted. Its bells rang and the paddle-wheeler backed away from the wharf and started a journey—Phil wished he knew where.

He spotted the *Lake Queen*, the steamer he was to take. Crowds of laborers, mostly Negroes and Irishmen, carried sacks of coal aboard. The Negroes sang at their work. On the side of a warehouse was a poster showing a picture of General Zachary Taylor. He was running. In one hand he gripped a sword, in the other the American flag. The poster read:

ZACHARY TAYLOR FOR PRESIDENT
(OLD ROUGH AND READY)
"HERO OF BUENA VISTA"

A man near Phil said, "I'm dead against Taylor. He was a good general but he's a slave owner." The man turned to Phil and said, "You going out on the *Lake Queen?*"

"Yes, sir. I'm headed for Buffalo."

"You're going the wrong way, boy. I mortgaged my farm and I'm westward bound. No money in the East. Just came from there."

Phil grinned. He ran his hand through his wavy black hair. Nothing in the world could prevent him from going to West Point.

When the *Lake Queen* paddled out into Lake Erie Phil sat at the stern to catch the June breeze. The wake of the steamboat formed an ever-changing pattern. Cleveland looked smaller as it dropped away. Near him sat a husky boy with broad shoulders. He looked about Phil's age. He was reading a book, *Scottish Chiefs*. The boy looked up.

"Hello," Phil said. "Are you traveling east?"

"Yes, I'm bound for West Point, New York. My name is Dave Stanley."

Phil opened his mouth. "Why, I'm going there, too." His dark eyes sparkled.

After they had shaken hands, Dave Stanley said, "How about the exams we have to take when we arrive? Do you think you'll pass? I hope so."

"I *have* to pass," Phil said. He did not say he was also worried over his lack of height. He was afraid to ask Dave what the height limit was.

Phil liked Dave Stanley. The big boy had a broad forehead, a large nose, and deep understanding eyes. He seemed completely at ease. It gave Phil confidence to be with someone who faced the same unknown.

When the *Lake Queen* arrived in Buffalo, Dave Stanley got out his barge ticket on the "Big Ditch." Phil had long planned to ride the train.

"I'll arrive in Albany before you," Phil said. "I want to visit my uncle there. Here's his address. I'll wait there for you, then we'll sail down the Hudson together."

Phil walked with Dave to the Erie Canal. Barges were lined up double, waiting for a chance to go ahead. Phil told his new friend good-bye and walked rapidly to the New York Central Railroad Station. There, puffing like a monster dragon, sending up a column of black smoke, stood the first steam engine Phil had ever seen. The engineer turned a valve and the huge funnel-shaped stack wheezed thin white smoke. Phil's heart pounded. He tried to act unconcerned as he studied the train and its amazing engine.

A bell clanged. "A-l-l a-board for Lock-port, Middle-port, Medina, Brock-port, Rochester . . . " The conductor took a deep breath and recited at the top of his lungs the stations east of Rochester. Phil listened intently. He did not want to take the wrong train. " . . . and All-bany!" the conductor shouted, "BOARD!" Phil felt nervous as he seated himself on a red plush seat beside a window. The monster wrenched itself and chuffed down the track, its bell clanging. The countryside flew by. The whistle shrieked. The wheels clicked a merry tune. They seemed to say, *"Going east, going east, going east."*

The palace steamer, *The New World,* throbbed along, leaving behind a wedge of white water as she plowed the Hudson River and the morning mists. The two boys sat on canvas stools on the forward deck, out of the hail of black cinders raining from the tall funnel.

A friendly passenger said, "Bound for West Point, eh? Son, on this river you'll see scenery the like of which you never saw before. I've been on every river you can call a river east of Saint Looey, and I'll take the Hudson first every time."

The New World sent a deep-throated warning to a sailboat. Another side-wheeler thrashed by. On its side, in gold letters six feet high, were the words, DE WITT CLINTON.

"That's the *De Witt Clinton,*" the man said. "Last month the pilot on her shot at the pilot on the *Napoleon.*

They had an argument down in New York City about which ship would dock where."

At noon a Negro in a white coat walked about the boat beating a small gong. "That means the dining room is open," Dave said.

The two boys descended the red-carpeted stairway and walked into the spacious dining room. In its center hung a huge, cut-glass chandelier that sent out rays of light. Yellow drapes bordered each window. White-coated Negro waiters stood near the spotless tables. Through the windows you could see the blue Hudson gliding by.

A waiter bowed slightly as he handed each boy a menu. Phil was amazed. No one had ever bowed to him before. He studied the menu. He felt confused over the choice of food. "I'll take a ham sandwich and a glass of milk," he said, finally.

"I'd like a beef steak and two baked potatoes," Dave said. "They tell me that the upperclassmen will give us a rough reception. I want to be fortified. Phil, do you think we'll be hazed?"

Phil coughed slightly. "I think I'll change my order. Give me a beef steak, too, please, and two baked potatoes, stewed tomatoes, string beans, corn on the cob, corn bread, and I'll take a glass of milk, please."

"How would you like your steak, sah?"

"I'd like it big," Phil said.

The waiter grinned, then repeated the boys' orders.

In the late afternoon *The New World* steamed into a wide bay. A passenger, standing on the texas deck near the boys, pointed to the right and said, "Newburgh. Newburgh was George Washington's headquarters for a time during the Revolutionary War. We're not stopping, the captain told me."

Phil's eyes popped. The sight of the town and the way the man talked made Phil feel as though the Revolutionary War were only a few years back.

"Down there," the passenger said to Phil, "are the Highlands of the Hudson. Yes, sir, the Highlands. This is Rip van Winkle country, boy. And you can throw in Hendrik Hudson. That big slope over there—that rocky one coming down to the water's edge—is Breakneck Ridge."

The New World steamed by a dingy paddle-wheeler towing five barges. "They're loaded with ice and hay for New York City," the passenger said.

The mountains rising on both sides of the Hudson made the steamboat seem tiny. The *thrash, thrash* of the paddle wheels echoed over the water from the huge granite mountain on the right. The shadow of the green mountain darkened the water.

"That's Storm King. Crow's Nest is on top," the man said to Phil. "And right down there is West Point."

"*Where?*" Phil failed to recognize the sound of his own voice.

"See where the river looks like it is blocked by that point of land?" the man answered. "That's West Point. The river makes a sharp turn there. It's the narrowest place on the river 'tween Albany and New York City. That's Constitution Island over on the left. Around there, General Washington placed the great chain to keep the British from coming up the river. Yes, sir, historical ground all around us—historical."

Phil tried to take in everything. He strained his eyes to see West Point.

The purser came up to the two boys. "Mr. Sheridan? You and Mr. Stanley are getting off soon. 'Bout fifteen minutes. When we reach Constitution Island, please come below to the starboard gangway. The cap'n says the tide isn't right to land you at the North Dock. He's puttin' you ashore in a rowboat."

All Phil could see of West Point was the Stars and Stripes flying from a sliver of a white flagpole above the trees. He thought, *I wish I could see more of it. This will be my home for the next four years—if I am tall enough and can pass.* In a burst of confidence, he said to Dave Stanley, "Do you know how tall a boy has to be to get in?"

"Yes. Five feet five."

Phil grinned. His big ears pushed back ever so slightly. His dark eyes shone. "That's exactly what I am," he said.

Bells clanged below. The two paddle wheels reduced their speed, then churned backward. The captain swung the nose of *The New World* to port.

"West Point! All ashore!" someone called from the bridge.

Phil picked up his carpetbag. He felt as though Somerset, Ohio, was a light year away.

Two sailors pulled Phil and Dave ashore in a rowboat. A war canoe shot by, eight young men in long-sleeved bathing suits at the paddles. "Those are cadets," one of the sailors said to Phil, "and there's one waiting for you at the wharf. See him? You think you can stand the hazing? I'm glad I don't have to face it."

CHAPTER 3

Halt! Who Goes There?

W HEN the two boys climbed the ramp of the dock, a West Point cadet in full-dress uniform approached them. The cadet's back was ramrod straight. He was immaculate. The brass buttons of his gray full-dress coat gleamed. The three gold stripes of a cadet lieutenant graced each of his shoulders. A stiff white collar pushed three-quarters of an inch above the collar of his gray coat. He wore a black, saucer-like forage cap, slanting downward toward a patent leather visor. He wore white gloves and his white trousers were starched so stiffly the creases looked like knife blades. "You're candidates?" he asked.

"Yep. I'm Phil Sheridan and this is Dave Stanley. We're from Ohio."

"I didn't ask for your life's history," the cadet snapped. "I'm down here on duty, picking up you animals. I have to see that you find a bed and some supper. Say 'sir' when you talk to an upperclassman."

"Yes, sir," Phil gasped. He felt as though he had walked into an icy shower.

"Pick up your bags and follow me."

"Yes, sir," both boys said.

The cadet cast a fishy eye at Phil. "Mister, how tall are you?"

"Five feet five, sir."

"You mean, 'five feet, five *inches.*' Plebes don't use slang or abbreviations. How much do you weigh?"

"One hundred and fifteen pounds, sir."

The cadet shook his head. "Our material gets poorer all the time," he said.

Phil clenched his fists, then deliberately unclenched them. Fighting an upperclassman would be a poor way to start a West Point career.

Halfway to the top of the steep hill, the cadet lieutenant pointed out a huge word cut into a granite ledge near the path: MEXICO. "General Winfield Scott is coming in a month to honor our graduates killed in Mexico. You'll see him, provided you pass the mental and physical exams."

Phil gripped his carpetbag tighter. He swallowed hard. A trickle of sweat ran down his brow. He knew it was not the steep climb that made him miserable, or even the cadet's rudeness. *Those exams!*

At the top, on the steps and porch of the boxlike Rider's Hotel, stood some ninety boys in civilian clothes. They gave a shout when they saw Phil and Dave. "Those *might* become your classmates if you're lucky," the cadet lieutenant said. His stress on the word did not make Phil feel happier.

"They're from every state in the Union," the cadet went on. "You'll stay with 'em in the hotel, and don't run all over the place. Tomorrow at eight the officers will round you up and march you to the adjutant. Then they'll check you over at the hospital. After that the professors will see how smart you are."

A cannon, fifty yards away, roared. Phil and Dave jumped. Black smoke belched over the green grass. The echoes of the explosion rumbled through the Highlands. The cadet lieutenant faced the flagpole and whipped his hand to the tip of his visor. The Hell Cats, the field music of the band—bugles, fifes, and drums—played retreat. Phil and Dave placed their caps over their hearts. Two enlisted men in full-dress blues lowered the flag slowly. It rested a moment on the branches of an elm, its thirty stars in sharp relief. The sound of the bugles made Phil's spine tingle. He uttered a silent prayer that he be allowed to follow that flag.

"I'm leaving you," the upperclassman said. He nodded toward the hotel.

"Thank you," Phil said, "er—er—sir."

"You never thank a man for doing his duty," the cadet said stiffly. Then he turned and headed across the green Plain toward cadet barracks.

Phil watched the upperclassman. "I don't know whether or not I agree with his last remark," he said to Dave.

Waiting in the hotel for the examination papers to be graded was nerve-racking. Rumors started. "You won't hear how you made out for five days," a bellboy said. "That's the rumor."

There were arguments among the boys about the correct way to do problems they had faced in algebra and plane geometry, and how to answer the questions in English and history.

Phil had no idea how well he had done. He stretched his legs on the path down toward the Hudson. He started along the rocky Flirtation Walk, but the sign NO ADMITTANCE UNLESS ACCOMPANIED BY A CADET stopped him. The view up the Hudson reminded him of pictures of a Norwegian fiord. He tried to think what he would do if he failed the entrance examinations. It suddenly occurred to him that he had not planned for failure.

At nine in the evening the adjutant, wearing the blue uniform of a lieutenant in the Corps of Engineers, assembled the ninety-seven candidates in the hotel's dining room. The lieutenant stood beside the piano. He said, "Give me your attention." The big room was silent. The officer drew a white paper from the top of his blouse and held it out before him at arm's length. His voice assumed a metallic quality as he read, "West Point, New York, June 30, 1848. Special Orders Number 87. The following named candidates, having successfully passed the mental and physical examinations, will take the required Oath and will be admitted on July 1, 1848 as cadets."

Phil held his breath. The alphabetical list seemed endless. The adjutant droned the names: " ... Phillips ... Robinson ... Rundell ... Sheridan ... Slocum ... Stanley ... " When the adjutant finished, Phil floated across the room and grabbed Dave Stanley's hand.

Half an hour later a slender boy with light-brown hair, eyes which slanted ever so slightly, and a prominent nose and chin knocked on the door of Phil's hotel room.

"You are Philip Sheridan, aren't you? I'm Hank Slocum, from New York. They just posted the roommate list downstairs. You and I are roommates. The other two are named Stanley and Davis." Hank Slocum grinned pleasantly. The boys shook hands. Phil liked Hank Slocum at first sight. He was glad to room with Dave Stanley, and Hank Slocum looked like a boy you could depend on.

The next day the candidates marched to the main room of the Academy's library. A huge portrait of Thomas Jefferson looked down at them. An officer lined up the boys and barked, "Attention!"

An old man wearing a blue uniform, with a sword clanking at his side, walked into the room. He was bald. A wide white beard stretched down to the top of his gold belt buckle. He was a strange-looking man. All he needed was a white nightgown and he would have looked like a prophet from the Old Testament. Phil wondered if the officer slept with his beard underneath or outside of the covers.

"I am Captain Brewerton, Superintendent, United States Military Academy," the officer said in a high-pitched voice. "I welcome each of you to West Point. You will find life here hard and challenging, but in the end your course will prove rewarding. The life of a soldier in the service of his country is not easy. We aim to prepare you for that life. My advice: learn the regulations and carry them out. Do not shirk your studies, for if you fall behind you may never catch up. After you have taken the Oath, you will be marched to the Treasurer, where you will turn in every cent you have. Your travel pay from your home to West Point will be credited to your account. Cadets are not permitted to have money. You are all on the same level whether you came here rich or poor. You will receive sixteen dollars a month pay. That, too, will be credited to your name. This pay will provide your books, uniforms, and meals. Again, young gentlemen, welcome." Captain Brewerton bowed his head slightly, smoothed his beard a moment while he eyed the new cadets, then clanked out of the library.

The first day as a cadet exhausted Phil. It seemed to him that he spent most of it on the run. He ran to the barber chair, where his long black hair was clipped. The barber paid no attention to Phil's directions. The aim seemed to be to scalp Phil and to get him out of the chair and another new cadet in. The path to the cadet store was lined with upperclassmen shouting, "Hurry! Hurry!" Phil carried a mattress to his room, at a dog-trot. He threw it on the floor, for there was no bed. He made three more trips on the run for blankets, sheets, a red comforter, a pillow, a gray raincoat, socks, underwear, a pair of black shoes, a forage cap, a full dress hat—the kind General Scott's men wore in the War of 1812—a brown linen jacket, a pair of gray trousers, white trousers, white gloves, a gray woolen jersey, and two laundry bags.

Phil's room, 721, was in confusion. It was a plain, bare room with a fireplace, two small tables, four wooden chairs, a large window, and two tall wooden lockers called "clothes presses." A small mirror rested on the mantel. Heaps of clothing and equipment were dumped about the floor.

The four plebes puzzled over a room arrangement card tacked to the back of the door. It read:

Blankets and sheets will be folded neatly at top of mattress. Mattress folded on the floor. Pillow on top of sheets. Blankets on top of pillow. Candle box (for scrubbing utensils) against wall under shelf nearest door. Underwear folded in folds five inches wide and placed on second shelf of clothes press, edges straight and bottom edge tangent to front of shelf. Lamp will be free from soot. It will be placed on center of mantel. Broom hanging behind door and free from dirt. Waste basket emptied daily at police call. Looking glass spotless and ...

A voice at the bottom of the iron stairs bellowed, "Attention, new cadets! Form out in front at once to draw arms!"

When the four roommates were back, they studied the room arrangement card again. *Muskets will be clean and ready for inspection at all times,* it read. *Cutlasses, bayonets, and swords if any, will hang over musket rack, points toward the window.*

The voice floated up the stairway. "New cadets will form in front of barracks in three minutes for infantry drill. Muskets and bayonets will be carried. New cadets will not use front doors of barracks. They will run around barracks."

Phil struggled into his short, tight-fitting brown linen jacket. The Infantry drill was exhausting. The upperclassmen demanded that every detail be executed with snap. The drill lasted for two hours, then the plebes were marched to supper.

When supper was finished, an upperclassman strode into

721. "New cadets will not light their lamps," he said sharply. "Get in bed at once. Hurry!"

When the upperclassman was gone Dave Stanley said, "I can't imagine us having to go to bed so early. I'm tired, but it's only quarter to seven."

Phil Sheridan did not answer. He pulled off his clothes. He unfolded his mattress on the floor and placed sheets on it. It was too warm for a blanket. He wished he had a bed for his mattress.

Hank Slocum said to the other roommate, "Davis, what do you think of our having to go to bed before seven?"

"I doan know," Davis drawled. "This is a strange place. I'm from No'th Carolina. Even the slaves and the chickens down there stay up later'n this."

A new cadet from across the hall walked in. When he saw Phil he laughed. "Are you fellows falling for that stuff?" he asked. "That upperclassman who ordered us to bed ran out of barracks and headed across the Plain. He's from summer camp. He has nothing to do with us. Our orders are to work on our muskets. If the grease isn't off of 'em and the screw heads clean by the inspection in the morning we can pick up four demerits. The drum doesn't sound taps till nine. My cousin, who graduated last year, told me about some of these tricks. That order to go to bed was just hazing."

Phil smiled to himself. *If that's hazing,* he thought, *I can take it.*

The next day, at the end of drill, a cadet lieutenant walked into 721, unbuttoned his dress coat, put his foot in Phil's chair, pushed his forage cap to the back of his head, and said, "Who in this room can swim? Raise your hand."

Phil's hand shot up.

"Humph," said the lieutenant. He indicated Cadets Stanley, Davis, and Slocum. "You three will receive swimming instruction later this summer. Mr. Sheridan, I want to see you swim now."

The upperclassman chuckled. He eyed the stout, wooden crossbar supporting the front end of the room's partition. "Strip to the waist, Mr. Sheridan, and climb up there. Lie on your stomach and start breast stroking. I want you to swim all the way to Newburgh and back. It's eleven miles one way, so pace yourself. You other plebes, your backs to the wall. Chins way back. More yet!" When Phil was stretched out on the crossbar, the upperclassman said, "Mr. Sheridan, don't fall, you'll hurt yourself. Come on! *Stroke—stroke—stroke!*"

Phil balanced himself on his stomach, eight feet above the floor. He was determined not to get angry. He went through the motions of the breast stroke. The upperclassman giggled. In a few minutes Phil's arms felt heavy. He shot a glance at his three roommates. They were flat against the wall, their eyes riveted on Phil.

"Take it easy, Mr. Sheridan," cautioned the upperclassman in a condescending voice. "Keep your balance. You've a long way to go. You just cleared Constitution Island."

Phil heard the faint click of a saber. The cadet lieutenant paid no attention. He said to Phil, "Come on. Kick your legs out like a frog, Mister."

Click! The noise was just outside the door. Phil jumped

lightly to the floor. The cadet lieutenant gasped in amazement. The door opened and an officer walked in. All the cadets in the room stood at attention. The cadet lieutenant turned white.

The Tactical Officer scanned each cadet.[1] "Mr. Sheridan," he said, "why are you without a shirt?" Before Phil could reply, the Tac said, "This will cost you two demerits. Put a shirt on at once."

The officer looked around the room, then left.

The upperclassman collapsed in Phil's chair. Beads of sweat appeared on his forehead. "Whew!" he said softly. "What a close one! I'm getting deaf, or I was concentrating too hard. If he had caught me hazing you, Mr. Sheridan, they would have turned me back to the next class. A year longer here—*wow!* Old Captain Brewerton is death on hazing."

The cadet lieutenant stood up. He was shaking. "I owe you my thanks," he said to Phil. The lieutenant stuck out his hand and Phil grasped it. "My name's Wilson," he said. "From now on we're friends."

Phil felt elated until he remembered the demerits he had received. "What about demerits?" he asked.

"You have a hundred and ninety-eight to go till next June thirtieth," Mr. Wilson said. "But you're going to receive few demos. I'll see to that. I have friends in this company, and I'm passing the word about what you did. Thanks again."

The "recognition" by Cadet Wilson reassured Phil. West

[1] Tactical Officer—an officer in charge of discipline. He also teaches military tactics to the cadets.

Point was a strange place, but with a cadet lieutenant on his side Phil felt he had a backer in high places.

The New Cadet Detail worked the plebes long hours. The day began when the reveille gun fired at ten minutes to five. It ended with three taps of the drum at nine. It was drill, drill, drill. The Tactical Officers were anxious that the plebes march as smartly as the upperclassmen.

"You will parade for General Scott at the end of the month," the Tacs explained. "Learn to march with your heads up."

But General Scott postponed his visit. When the plebes ended the first part of their apprenticeship, they were marched a mile across the Plain to summer camp. The hazing started all over again.

Summer camp, a neat tent village, stood on the site of old Fort Clinton, part of the West Point defenses in the Revolutionary War. Every wall tent was occupied by two cadets. The tents had a floor and rough wooden furniture. Phil liked living under canvas. At night it was cooler than in barracks. But for plebes the trouble with summer camp was the upperclassmen.

One night while Phil was asleep a blanket was thrown over him and he was tied down to his canvas cot. He was carried out in the street. He freed himself in ten minutes and jumped up, determined to fight his tormentors, but there was no one in sight.

When the plebes got a chance to speak to each other, all they talked about were their experiences while on guard. Each cadet, as part of his training, had to walk sentry duty. Upperclassmen not on guard hazed the plebe sentinels almost nightly. Men covered with sheets approached a sentry in the dead of night. In answer to the plebe's challenge, "Halt! Who goes there?" the "spook" would answer, "The Queen of Sheba," or "The United States Frigate Constitution," or "The Devil in a chariot drawn by four mud turtles." The poor plebes confronted by such odd answers were confused as to how to proceed with the sentinels' ritual.

The hazing grew worse. Plebe sentinels were captured and stripped of their uniforms. Others had their muskets wrenched away. Some were gagged and tied to trees. Three upperclassmen caught hazing sentinels by the Tacs were banned from West Point for a year—turned back to join the next class. There was no mourning for the three offenders by the plebe class. The hazing stopped for a week, then started again.

One night Phil was a member of the guard. He sat in the guard tent munching "guard sandwiches"—slices of cold beef between thick pieces of bread. About the little table were other members of the third relief. Yellow candlelight played on their faces. Wax streaked down the candle, filled the pewter candle-holder, and trickled onto the table. The plebes were unhappy. The third relief walked post from 3 to 5 A.M. This was the hour when upperclassmen bent on hazing left their beds and raided the sentinels. Phil poured each man a cup of strong black coffee.

The corporal of the relief walked briskly into the tent. The plebes sprang to attention.

"Rest!" the corporal said, and the plebes relaxed. "They just took the clothes off the sentinel on Post Number Four," the corporal went on. "They hung his musket and bayonet fifty feet high in a tree. The Officer of the Day will report the plebe for losing his weapons. That plebe'll get ten demerits."

It was three-thirty in the morning. Phil Sheridan trod up and down the grassy path along the top of Fort Clinton parapet. The dew made his feet wet, but the night was entrancing. A billion stars twinkled. The moon, in its last quarter, hung just over old Fort Putnam up on the hill. The shadows under the elms along Post Number Four were deep and mysterious. Every tent in camp was dark except the four guard tents. Candlelight made them dull red pyramids. A steamboat, rounding Gee's Point, gave a deep-throated whistle. Phil looked over his shoulder every few steps. He was determined not to be hazed. A cattle barge, loaded with live calves for New York City, slipped down the Hudson, its cargo bleating. In fifteen minutes the night was silent again.

Phil caught a glimpse of a shadowy form running across the far end of his post. He brought his musket down to port arms and shouted, "Halt! Who's there?" There was no answer. *Was I dreaming?* Phil thought. Down the road at the bottom of the parapet's slope, a figure covered with a sheet crouched under a bush. Phil challenged it. There was no answer. He was in a quandary. *Is that figure off my post? Should I run down there? A sentinel cannot desert his post.*

Phil was about to call for the corporal of the guard when he heard a footstep behind him. He brought his musket down to his hip with a crash. He whirled. The sharp point of his bayonet gleamed in the starlight. Ten feet away stood a cadet with a black mask over his face. A forage cap was jammed tightly down on top of the mask. From the man's hands hung a rope.

Phil charged. He swung the butt of his musket upward with all his might. The musket grazed his assailant's chin. The toe of the musket caught the visor of the forage cap and flipped it over the man's head. The masked cadet jumped backward and ran. Phil speared the forage cap with his bayonet, held it toward the sky, and shouted at the top of his lungs, "Corporal of the Guard! Post Number Four!"

Phil made his report and gave the corporal the ruined forage cap.

"You could have broken the fellow's jaw," the corporal said.

"He could have tied me up," Phil answered.

"You're no diplomat," the corporal said. "You're a fighter."

Phil was bothered no more by upperclassmen.

But when academics started in September, Phil *was* bothered.

10125

CHAPTER 4

The Plaque Without a Name

THE academic pace whizzed. It moved far faster than Phil had visualized back in Somerset. Colonel Thayer, the great West Point educator-superintendent, had set the pattern sixteen years before when he decided there would be eight cadets to an instructor. *But the trouble is,* Phil thought, *in an hour's time the instructor finds how little you know.*

Trigonometry and logarithms were mysteries. And in English the instructor lowered the marks on compositions for each misspelled word.

At the end of the first month the class standings were published on the bulletin boards in the sallyport. Phil stood dangerously near the bottom of his class. His marks were poor. He was frightened, for cadets who made unsatisfactory grades were dismissed from the Academy. Dave Stanley tried to help, but he lacked the knack of being a good coach. Matt Davis, of North Carolina, had all he could do to stay in the middle of the class.

Hank Slocum watched Phil's inch-along progress. One

evening when the four friends were undressing for bed, Hank said, "Phil, I had oodles of math up in Cazenovia Seminary. Let me try to coach you—in everything but your spelling. You'll have to do that."

Just then the Hell Cats played taps on the drum. All lamps went out. Phil and Hank waited until the cadet in charge of quarters inspected, then they sprang out of bed and hung a blanket over the window. The other two roommates rested uneasily on their mattresses because of the lamplight and the hum of voices at the table, but they did not complain. They were anxious that the hot-tempered Irishman become proficient in his studies.

Suddenly Phil and Hank thought they heard footsteps in the division of barracks. They blew out the lamp, jerked down the blankets, and popped into bed. The Tactical Officer cast the light of his bull's-eye lantern about and left. When all was quiet the two friends resumed their work.

Phil's marks improved slowly. He stayed at the Academy by dint of hard work.

Winter at West Point was bitter. It seemed colder than in Ohio. Icy winds swept down the frozen Hudson and across the snows of the Plain. A few cadets violated orders by crossing over the frozen river to Garrison, and were reported. Oxen driven by enlisted men hauled snowplows about the post to keep the roads open. But the dullness of winter was broken when General Scott sent word from Washington that he was finally coming to West Point.

The Military Academy became a beehive. Cadets and enlisted men labored with shovels and horse-drawn carts to clear snow from the area behind barracks so that the Corps could parade for the Army's senior general.

When the big day arrived in February, the temperature dropped to six above. Standing in formation, the Corps wore long gray overcoats, but the wind made the coats feel like cotton. Phil's ears tingled. When General Scott appeared with Captain Brewerton, the wind swept up snow from a nearby pile and plastered the two officers. Phil shivered as the wind blasted the four companies of cadets.

General Scott was even larger than Phil expected. He stood six feet seven and weighed over two hundred and fifty pounds. He was sixty-two, but his wrinkled face and side whiskers made him look eighty. He wore a brown muskrat hat tapering to a chisel point. A blue overcoat with gold epaulets and brass buttons covered his frame. At his side, from a gold sword belt, hung a golden sword. The size of the sword reminded Phil of a Crusader's weapon.

After the general returned the salute of the first captain, he lumbered down the line of cadets with Captain Brewerton. Phil braced. He stared straight to the front. While the general inspected, the band struck up "The Grand Canal," a piece it played in New York City at the celebration of the opening of the Erie Canal. Phil felt like a world traveler, for he had seen that grand canal. He loved the West Point band. He wiggled his toes to the beat of the bass drum. He could understand why, in ancient combat, bands accompanied troops into battle.

When the general and Superintendent were back in the center facing the cadets, the boy next to Phil whispered, "Be ready, Phil."

The adjutant gave a command, and five cadets from each class formed in line in front of the Colors of the Corps and marched straight to the front. Phil strutted; he was proud to be one of the selected cadets. The special cadets halted in front of the general and saluted. The old general returned their salutes slowly. Phil forgot the cold.

General Scott half-turned and motioned with a fur gauntlet. Out from behind him marched a file of twenty enlisted men. Each carried a captured Mexican battle flag. Each selected cadet received a flag. The wind fought Phil and the nineteen other cadets carrying the flags back to the Corps. The flags cracked in the wind and whipped straight out. Phil was proud. He felt that the eyes of the Corps were on him.

That night he wrote:

WEST POINT
February 17, 1849

Dear Sister,

The general was here today. I suppose you read in the papers of the reception of the 20 colors taken during the Mexican War. I carried a flag taken at Chaputopeck. It was tattered by balls.

Cadet Phil H. Sheridan

P.S. Excuse me for being pompous in signing my name.

Phil checked his letter for misspelled words. He was not sure of "Chapultepec," but it looked pretty good. He admired his letter; it would cause a sensation in Somerset. He hoped his sister would show it to the crowd in Mr. Dittoe's store.

The next day the cadets marched into the chapel near the library. After them marched the officers of the Academic and Tactical Departments. Now came a strange procession.

Some of the strangers wore uniforms, but most of them had on civilian overcoats. Some limped. Four thumped down the aisle on crutches. Several had empty sleeves. A tall man held his head in a peculiar fashion while his sister guided him. These were veterans of the Mexican War. They were living lessons in the awfulness of war. Until he saw these veterans, Phil thought it would be glamorous to be wounded.

The chapel, with its six ivory-white Doric columns and high ceiling, was crammed. The black and gold plaques on the wall to the right thrilled Phil. They bore the names of heroes of the Revolutionary War: MAJOR GENERAL NATHANAEL GREENE, ISRAEL PUTNAM, HENRY KNOX, FRANCIS MARION, JAMES CLINTON, ANTHONY WAYNE, PHILIP SCHUYLER, HORATIO GATES, WILLIAM MOULTRIE . . .

A glass box cut into the wall on the other side bore a stand of nine colors. Near them hung new plaques bearing the names of officers killed in the Mexican War. General Scott had come to honor those names.

The ponderous general and the Superintendent walked down the aisle. The wooden pew creaked when the general sat down. Captain Brewerton walked onto the podium at the center of a low, red-carpeted stage. The old captain's beard waggled while he talked. Phil found this distracting.

Now General Scott spread his notes on the podium. Close up, he seemed even bigger than at parade. His bushy white hair hung almost to his tremendous shoulders. His white side whiskers, black eyebrows, and deep-set eyes gave him a fierce look, but his voice was kind. "Thank you, Captain Brewerton," he said.

Scott bowed his head slightly at the group of officers and smiled at the cadets. He said to the officers, "Brothers who fought in Mexico." Then he began to talk, not to the officers but to the cadets. "I admire cadets," he said. "I understand you. Maybe some of your officers don't. When I retire from active duty, I'm going to make my home right here in the hotel so I can be near you. I like cadets because in you lies the defense of our nation." Phil was scarcely breathing.

The giant waved his hand at the new plaques on the left wall. "These plaques bear the names of officers who gave their lives in battle for our country. I knew many of them. Some are from this school. I am not a West Pointer, but I pay tribute to your graduates. Without West Point graduates my army, multiplied by four, could not have set foot in Mexico City."

The General looked at the plaques at the back of the chapel. "I roamed this chapel shortly after it was built, twelve years ago," he went on. "There was a plaque with the name scotched out. Is that plaque still there, Captain Brewerton?"

Brewerton nodded his bald head. "Yes, sir. In the gallery, up there."

General Scott thundered, "That plaque carries a lesson. I won't foul the air by mentioning the man whose name is blanked out. Once he was General Washington's best fighter. Gold and high living were the rattlesnake's weakness. For gold, the traitor tried to sell West Point to the enemy." Scott's cavernous eyes blazed. He hit the podium a blow. His notes danced. Phil scrunched in his seat. He expected the general to curse. "Gold meant too much to that man," the general said.

"The love of gold can be a sin. Because of the discovery of gold last year in California, thousands and thousands are traveling west across the plains through Indian country. In some army units soldiers have stolen horses and rifles and lit out for the gold streams. In times like these officers must hold their units together."

The general gripped the podium and leaned toward the cadets. "Our army is small, but it means much. Its best leaders in and out of ranks are inspired by love of country." The general gathered up his notes. "Units led by love of country are the best," he said. "They do not fail. I leave that thought with you. Perhaps there will come a time when you will need it."

Back in 721, alone, Phil thought over the general's words. He lit up a tiny, curved meerschaum pipe, his last purchase in Fink and Dittoe's store. The bowl, just below his chin, held only two thimbles of tobacco, but the pipe was a comfort. It reminded him of home. "Led by love of country," Phil whispered. He thought again of Ohio. "I love that country," he said aloud. *Benedict Arnold's nameless plaque—it was awful to think what might have happened had the traitor been successful in selling West Point.*

Life at West Point continued to be a struggle between Phil and the Academic Departments, but when Phil was a yearling—a sophomore—a cadet entered the Corps from Virginia whom Phil did not like. And when Phil was a senior the friction boiled to a head.

CHAPTER 5

Fix Bayonets!

THE trouble was that the cadet from Virginia, Bill Terrill, spoke in a haughty manner. Phil began to hate Terrill. There was only one good thing about the Virginian: he disliked slavery. But when Terrill was on duty he had a mean, snippy way of talking.

Phil avoided him, but when Phil was a senior—a "first classman" in West Point talk—Terrill was promoted to cadet sergeant. Phil was not given chevrons, and this rankled.

Phil talked over his dislike for the Virginian with his friend, George Crook. Cadet Crook said, "Don't get your dander up, Phil. Take it easy."

"But I can't stand the way he talks when we're in ranks," Phil said. "He speaks in a rude, raw manner. His authority has gone to his head. I've had enough."

At parades, Terrill became unbearable. Part of his duty, while marching in the file closers, was to make corrections, and he made them in tones dripping with acid.

One broiling September afternoon the cadet battalion

formed for full-dress parade in the road in front of barracks. The quartermaster watering cart had sprinkled the
dust a half-hour before, but the street looked as if it had
never tasted water. The band, marching to the taps of a
Hell Cat's drum, strutted onto the parade ground at the
far end of the Plain. The musicians halted and waited for
the time to sound Adjutant's Call. The parade ground was
baked brown. West Point had seen no rain for almost a
month. A cloud hovered over Crow's Nest, but it avoided
West Point and floated across the Hudson to Cold Spring.
The deep-blue sky seemed merciless. There was no chance
of rain. It was hot.

Beads of perspiration oozed from under Phil's heavy
tarbucket hat and coursed down his red cheeks. His full-
dress coat gripped him like a vise. The brass buttons on the
gray coat reflected the sun.

The cadet captain of "C" Company whipped out his
sword. He shouted, "Com-pan-ee, atten—tion! Right step,
march! One, two—one, two . . ."

Phil gripped his musket. It felt heavier than usual. He
sidestepped with the rest of the company.

"Com-pan-ee, halt!" barked the captain.

From the file closers came Terrill's rasping voice. "Sir,
Mr. Sheridan, you did that poorly—*very* poorly. You were
way out of step. Understand?"

Phil gritted his teeth. He wished he had been harder on
the uppity Mr. Terrill two years ago when Mr. Terrill
was a plebe. It seemed a rank injustice that Terrill was now
a sergeant.

The cadet captain commanded loudly, "Parade, rest!
Fix bayonets!" One hundred shiny, triangular bayonets

clicked into place on the ends of "C" Company's muskets.

"Slow again, Mister Sheridan," Terrill said. "Are you asleep, sir? All you men along here, stand up! You're slouching, all of you. Brace!"

Phil held on to himself. He did not brace.

The captain commanded, "C Company, right dress!"

The company flicked heads and eyes to the right. Each man in ranks grasped his musket below the stacking swivel and inched up on the imaginary line between the right and left guides.

"Dress back, Mister Sheridan," Terrill snapped. "You are ahead of the line, sir. Brace up, sir."

He's putting that "sir" on to keep within bounds, thought Phil. "I am on line," Phil said sharply. "You must not speak to me in ranks."

"Don't talk back to me, sir. No talking in ranks," snapped Bill Terrill. "I tell you, dress back, Sheridan. Now you do as I say and be quick about it."

Something inside Phil broke. He elbowed his way through the rear rank to the file closers. Terrill was standing at attention, only twelve feet away. Phil whipped his musket to the position of *charge bayonets*. The sun glistened on the dangerous weapon. He aimed the bayonet at Terrill's chest. "Damn you, sir," Phil snarled, "I will run you through."

The Virginian did not move. "Run ahead," he said quietly.

Phil charged. Suddenly, he stopped. The point of the bayonet quivered three inches from Bill Terrill's chest. Terrill stood like a statue. Something stayed Phil's hand.

He did not run Terrill through. He was to be forever grateful. He lowered his musket.

"Sheridan! Get back in ranks!" shouted the cadet captain.

Adjutant's Call sounded. Phil obeyed. He was trembling with anger, but he took his place in ranks. The band struck up "The Dashing White Sergeant."

It was a parade Phil did not remember. He went through his part as if he were in a dream. After parade, in his room, Phil ripped open his full-dress coat and slumped in his chair. His temples pounded. He was still angry over Terrill's criticisms and his rude tone.

Dave Stanley and George Crook came in. "Phil," George said, "I was down at the company office. Bill Terrill just wrote up a report on you. They say there'll be an investigation. Why don't you go see Terrill and apologize?"

"Apologize?" snapped Phil. "Applesauce! I'm no politician." Phil placed his musket in its rack and took off his full-dress coat. He stepped to the door. "I am going to get that Virginian," he said.

"No, Phil!" Stanley said. "Stay here." But Phil Sheridan thrust Dave aside and darted out of the room and clattered down the iron stairway.

"Where's Terrill?" Phil demanded from a group of cadets at the bottom of the staircase.

"He's sitting on the front steps," someone answered.

Phil dashed out the door. Bill Terrill had his back half turned. Phil tore at his enemy. When Phil was almost on Terrill, Phil shouted a warning, "Damn you, Terrill!"

Bill Terrill jumped. Phil struck him with all his might on the right shoulder. Terrill stepped back and shot a left into Phil's face. Terrill stood a head taller than Phil. Phil struck Terrill again on the shoulder. The Virginian rained blows on Phil and knocked him down the steps. Phil scrambled to his feet. His dark eyes were blazing. His fists were clenched. His chest heaved. Two classmates grabbed him, preventing him from charging again at Terrill.

That night Phil did not study. He was still angry, and before him was a small piece of white paper. He had to answer it. Phil read Terrill's report for the twentieth time:

West Pont, N. Y., Sept. 9, 1851

Cadet reported	Offense
Sheridan, P. H.	Insubordinate conduct, replying to a file closer in a highly insulting and disrespectful manner; violating paragraph 134 Academic Regulations: fighting.

Attached to the report was Bill Terrill's statement:

I, being a file closer, did order Cadet Sheridan to dress back; whereupon he turned around and said, "you must not speak to me in ranks, Mr. Terrill," and if I remember rightly I said, "stop talking in ranks." Cadet Sheridan broke through the rear rank and ran toward me with his bayonet lowered and said, "damn you, sir. I will run you through." I stood still and told him to "run ahead." I told him if it were not for my office I would strike him down. He said, "damn you. I do curse you." I told him I would report him, and the company was marched to parade.

Relative to the fighting, I acted in self defense. I was not aware of Mr. Sheridan's approach until a second before he struck me. I do not think I could have acted otherwise, without reflecting upon my character as a gentleman.

Respectfully Submitted
William R. Terrill
Cadet (Sgt) "C" Comp.

To Capt. B. R. Alden
    Comd'g Corps Cadets

Phil labored over his excuse. He wrote it for the tenth time:

I was spoken to by the file closer in an improper tone. I was ordered by him to dress when I was accurately dressed. The file closer had been making use of his authority to opress files in ranks, by speaking to them improperly, unnecesarily, and continually, and as confirmation of this, I respectfully refer the Comdt. to any of the cadets on the right of "C" Company.

Phil showed his paper to his roommates. "What do you think of this?" he asked.

Matt Davis and Dave Stanley said, "It's too short."

Hank Slocum said, "You misspelled 'oppress' and 'unnecessarily.' I agree. You'll have to say more."

Phil did not correct the words. He snatched the paper and ran angrily out of the room. He headed for the company's office to turn in his answer.

That night Phil studied late with Hank Slocum. But Phil made no progress. Phil kept wondering: *What will they do with me?* He had never been so worried.

The next morning Phil did not go to class. He was interviewed by the company Tactical Officer, who passed him on to the Commandant of Cadets.

Phil told the Commandant of Mr. Terrill's caustic tongue, which cut every cadet private in C Company. The Commandant listened, then said, "Do you think that is an excuse for you to threaten a person with a bayonet?"

Phil did not answer. He still felt angry when he thought of Terrill.

"Get in your full-dress uniform," the Commandant said, "and report to the Superintendent."

Phil's hand shook as he tapped on the door of the Superintendent's office. When Phil stood before the Superintendent's desk and saluted, his knees trembled.

"You are in serious trouble, Mr. Sheridan," the elderly Superintendent said. "We cannot have cadets breaking ranks and challenging other cadets with bayonets. It's barbaric. You fought Mr. Terrill because he reported you. Is that correct?"

"Yes, sir."

"Hm-m-m." Captain Brewerton tugged at his beard. He looked more severe than Moses. He got up and paced up and down the side of the office. He looked out at the Hudson, where an old side-wheeler struggled upstream towing a string of empty barges. Phil, at attention, kept his eyes straight to the front.

"Up until now," the captain said, "your record has been excellent. You have not made high marks in the last three

years, but you've worked. You have received few demerits.
You are one of the best in your class in horsemanship. But
you lose your temper."

Phil felt as though he were on a pair of scales being
weighed.

"Um-m-m—humph," the Superintendent continued. "I
can settle this matter by placing you before a court-martial,
sir, or I can make my recommendation and refer the affair
to the Chief of Engineers in Washington. Which do you
prefer?"

Phil took a long breath. He wished he knew what Captain Brewerton might write the Chief of Engineers. Phil
licked his lips. They were bone dry. "Sir," he finally managed to say, "I do not want a court-martial."

Captain Brewerton nodded. "That's all, Mr. Sheridan."

A month dragged by. Every day was torture; Phil wondered constantly what "Washington" would decide. It
seemed as though he would never hear his fate. He wrote
home about his trouble. His mother answered promptly,
scolding him, but consoling him at the same time. His
father did not write. Phil's roommates and friends worried,
too.

"What will you do if they discharge you?" Dave Stanley
asked Phil.

"I will enlist."

Hank Slocum said, "Suppose they won't—" Then he
stopped.

Phil knew. *Suppose they won't let me enlist because of
my temper?* This worried him more.

One noon in the mess hall, in mid-October, the cadet
adjutant called the Corps of Cadets to attention. The adju-

tant published the orders for the guard detail, then held a piece of paper at arms' length. The huge room became deathly quiet. Even the waiters stopped. Phil's heart jumped. *This is my lot,* he thought.

"Attention to orders!" shouted the adjutant. "Headquarters, West Point, New York. For threatening another cadet with a bayonet, said cadet being in performance of his duties, and for fighting said cadet for reporting him, Cadet Philip H. Sheridan, Class of 1852, will rusticate for one year. He will proceed to his home. On July 1, 1852 he will report to the adjutant, United States Military Academy, and will join the Class of 1853. While rusticating for a year, Cadet Sheridan will receive the pay of a cadet. By order of the Secretary of War. Rest!"

Phil stood up. Every eye in the mess hall fastened on him. He picked up his forage cap from the shelf underneath his chair and walked out of the mess hall like a person in a trance. He was so mad he did not trust himself to speak to anyone for an hour. The year's penalty seemed most unfair.

He told his friends good-bye. When he walked across the path to Rider's Hotel, West Point looked more beautiful than he had ever seen it. The maples and elms bordering the Plain were vivid scarlet and pale yellow. The air was crisp. He drank in every detail of the scene. A steamboat rounding Gee's Point whistled. Phil tightened his grip on his carpetbag and sprinted for the steep path to the North Dock.

The penalty year in Somerset passed slowly. Mr. Dittoe gave Phil his old job back behind the counter. Phil was sur-

prised: the townspeople did not tease him about his punishment. When the time finally rolled around for him to leave
home again, his father accompanied him once more to the
stagecoach station in front of Finch's Tavern.

Phil's father said, "Ye had a bitter lesson. I hope it *is* a
lesson. I hope ye will niver again lose control of your
temper."

"I won't," Phil promised.

"We all love you, Phil. Good luck."

Phil wondered why he felt closest to his father when he
was telling him good-bye.

The team pulling the stagecoach pranced down the main
street. Phil kissed his father good-bye, climbed aboard, and
headed east.

He timed his travel to arrive at West Point on graduation day. It was exciting. Crowds of relatives and friends
hovered about the new second lieutenants. The trees around
the Plain were dark green. The scene was beautiful. It was
wonderful to see his friends again—Dave Stanley, Hank
Slocum, Matt Davis—but when they put on their blue
officer's uniforms and left Phil felt as if the bottom had
dropped out of life.

George Crook and John Nugent came up. "We waited
for you, Phil," George said. "Let's have our picture taken.
Three boys from Ohio."

That afternoon, when the new graduates had gone and
the Post was quiet, Phil ran across Bill Terrill. When Phil
saw the cadet who had cost him a year, Phil felt a surge
of anger. He clenched his fists, then relaxed them. "Hello,"
he said flatly.

"Hello," said Terrill.

Phil decided that he would never again speak to Bill Terrill.

That night three unusual cadets called on Phil. He knew one of them, James Birdseye McPherson, of Ohio. McPherson put out his hand with an easy grin. "I came to welcome you to our class, Phil. I have Hood and Stuart here." McPherson's eyes twinkled. "Two Southerners," he said.

Phil knew McPherson was one of the most popular men in the Corps. He was also first in the class in studies. Phil bristled inwardly when he looked at the two Southerners, for he disliked most people from the South. He forced a smile.

"I remember you well, Mr. Hood," Phil said.

Hood, blond with blue eyes sunk deep in their sockets, shoved out a huge hand and bowed. "Thank you. Glad to have you in our class," he drawled.

McPherson clapped the other Southerner on the shoulder. "This is James E. B. Stuart. He and John Hood are two wildcats. 'Beauty' Stuart is in the second class."

Phil looked up at the three cadets. McPherson looked like a friendly scholar, Hood like a fighter. Stuart's wide forehead, straight nose, kindly eyes, and weak chin made him look like anything but a wildcat.

On the battlefield, years later, Phil remembered the meeting. The Southerners, John Hood and "Beauty" Stuart, proved to be leaders in action, but Jim McPherson and Phil Sheridan were wildcats, too.

CHAPTER 6

The Big Question

WHEN his West Point graduation day finally arrived, Phil pulled on his second lieutenant's uniform with high hopes. The blue uniform seemed to hold the promise of excitement. He was tired of schoolwork. He hated to say good-bye to his cadet friends, but he had friends in the service. A letter from George Crook told of his adventures in Oregon. Phil was eager to begin life as a second lieutenant.

After three months' leave at home, his orders arrived.

> Second Lieutenant Sheridan will report at the completion of his leave to the Adjutant, Newport Barracks, Kentucky, for recruiting duty. On March 15, 1854, Lieutenant Sheridan will report for duty to the commanding officer, 1st Infantry Regt., Fort Duncan, Texas, Mexican border.

The Mexican border! Phil's dark eyes brightened. He could see Indians, bandits, soldiers, buffalo, hazardous journeys. He looked up Fort Duncan on a map. It was a pinpoint opposite the Mexican town of Piedras Negras.

Phil's mother worried. "That's Indian country," she said. Phil's father told his friends proudly, "Phil's been ordered to Texas. They need officers like Phil down there."

When the wagon train in which Phil was a passenger jolted its way across Texas, Phil discovered life on the plains was not as glamorous as he had thought. From his seat on a sack of grain in a crowded covered wagon, he could see only the next wagon in the procession, and the laboring mules pulling it. The constant creak of the wagon and the snap and squeak of the harness were far more irritating than the crack of the halyards on the sailing vessel that carried him across the Gulf and down the Inside Passage from New Orleans to Corpus Christi.

His cramped space in the canvas-topped wagon made his trip down the Ohio and Mississippi Rivers seem more luxurious than it had been. He wished he were back in gay New Orleans. He pulled a book out of his bag, but the lurch of the wagon made it impossible to read.

The nights were cool. After supper, Phil left the campfire, tugged on a buffalo-robe coat his teamster lent him, and joined the scouts on the outside of the circle formed by the twenty-one wagons. "Don't travel out beyond the scouts," the train commander cautioned. " 'Tain't healthy. Could be Indians."

Finally the train conquered the long miles and creaked into the forlorn town of Laredo. Phil was disappointed in the Rio Grande, for it looked like a trickle compared to the Hudson. At a nearby army post Phil borrowed a six-mule team, a teamster, a wagon, and two mounted infantrymen. "This ought to speed you through to Duncan," the officers said.

The six-mule team yanked the wagon through the sage-brush and around cactus, thirty-five miles a day, but the sameness of the land tired Phil. The March wind kicked up clouds of dust. Every once in a while white-tailed deer raced across the wagon's path, and occasionally, off in the distance, you glimpsed antelope. Several times a day the mules kicked up coveys of quail. The birds sailed leisurely a hundred yards or so, then put down. Phil wanted to hunt, but the driver pressed on.

Every few hours they rolled by a cross, or crosses, about three feet high. They were made of sticks lashed together with rawhide and stuck into the earth. When they passed one the teamster pointed with his whip and said, "Comanches," or "Lipans," or "Apaches." The crude crosses sent shivers up and down Phil's spine. "Dangerous along here a few years back," the driver said. "We'd have had ten mounted men escortin' us 'stead of two."

Late on the eighteenth day from the Gulf the rider a half-mile to the front turned in his saddle and waved his musket. *Indians,* Phil thought. He pulled his pistol.

"Take it easy," the teamster said. "It's the Wilkerson ranch."

The mules sensed water and better food. They galloped, and Phil grasped the side of his seat to keep from being tossed off.

The Wilkerson ranch was not Phil's idea of a ranch. Its five flat-topped adobe buildings squatted on the top of a lonely ridge. Behind the shacks stood a small corral containing four ponies, a well with a windlass, three wagons, one of them broken, five goats and some chickens. The center adobe hut had a garden of cactus bordered with stones.

The ranch looked desolate. The deep-blue sky and the sage-brush seemed to emphasize the lonesomeness.

The teamster pointed to a creek bottom a mile away. "Down there in the cottonwoods is Dan Wilkerson nursin' his herd—'bout forty longhorns. Good old Dan."

A woman appeared at the doorway of the largest adobe building, wiped her hands on her apron, and disappeared. Dan Wilkerson left his cattle and galloped toward his home.

When the rancher reined his pony at the wagon, he touched the rim of his wide-brimmed hat. The teamster tossed Wilkerson a box. "Cigars with the cap'n's compliments," he said. "This here is Lieutenant Sheridan, bound fer Duncan."

Dan Wilkerson's wind-etched face broke into a grin. "Great to meet you folks," he said. "Climb down off that rocker box. We'll give my wife a few minutes more to pretty up, then we'll all have coffee. Stay here tonight." He squinted at the sky. "Too late for you to push on. You must be tired of campin'. We'll roast a goat."

Phil jumped down, and the rancher swung out of the saddle. He towered over Phil. The teamster caught Wilkerson's look and said, with a nod at Phil, "He's not the biggest man I ever hauled, but he'll do to ride to the river with. I like him excellently well."

"Glad to hear it," Wilkerson said. He pumped Phil's hand. His drawl was soft and melodious as he said, "We haven't had a visitor here in a month, if you don't count the Fort Duncan patrol. They drop in on us every Wednesday at noon, reg'lar as clockwork. We ran off a horse thief last Thursday, but you'd hardly count him."

At the supper table, the Wilkersons and their cowboy pumped Phil for information. Wilkerson was the only one who had ever heard of West Point. Phil talked of life at the Academy, but he did not mention Bill Terrill. He was ashamed now of fighting Terrill and of the year the quarrel had cost.

Mrs. Wilkerson was interested in the dances the cadets held at Christmas and in June. "They must be lovely," she said. She looked at Phil's long, black, wavy hair. "Did you have any particular girl?"

Phil's ruddy face became an even brighter red. "No, ma'am. I am not very social," he said. "I'm strictly an outdoors man."

"Sociability won't bother you along this border," the rancher said. "There's some girls in Eagle Pass, but most of 'em just causes trouble. Some of the boys don't pay any mind to the army rules, and skin over into Mexico on occasion to Fuente for a bucket of blue water—beer that is—but it ain't recommended."

Wilkerson placed another forkful of goat meat on Phil's plate. The meat was tasty. Phil mopped his plate with a crust of cornbread.

"There's a thousand mile of border," Wilkerson drawled. "I love this country, but it needs policing so we Texicans can live without death hoverin' just around the bend. We have wild horses, wild mules, wild cattle, wild Indians, wild Mexicans crossin' over, and wild white men. They're the worst. The Mexicans and white trash driftin' around challenge the Texas Rangers. Our Rangers are good, but they ought to be tripled. They ride like Mexicans, shoot like Tennesseeans, and fight like devils, but they ain't enough of 'em. Take the Army. It's got a dozen little measly posts strung along a thousand mile of river. The Army's here for protection against Indians, but it can't do the job entirely."

Phil looked at the rancher's pistol hanging in its holster from a spike on the back of the door. There was a heavy-caliber rifle resting on a rack of deer horns on the wall back of Mrs. Wilkerson. "I'll need a pony, won't I?" Phil asked.

" 'Deed you will," Wilkerson said. "If they don't give you one up at Duncan, you come down here and I'll catch you one and help you gentle it."

Wilkerson's cowboy shoved his three-legged stool back from the table and pulled on a pair of worn leather chaps and a sheepskin coat. He leaned over Phil's shoulder and picked up two chops of meat and stuck them into the pocket of his coat. "I'm ridin' till daylight," he said. "This snack'll come in good about two in the morning when I'm tired from singing to the herd."

When the cowhand had gone, Wilkerson poked at the fire in the stick and mud chimney. Ashes floated over his boots and the hearth. He took up a bundle of twigs and scratched the hard, adobe hearth. He seized a book from a hand-turned hickory chair with a rawhide seat, and ripped pages from the book. He stuck the pages under the mes-quite log in the fireplace and fanned the fire and blew at it. The flame ate the pages of the book and bit into the log. The firelight made the wrinkles in Wilkerson's face look deeper. The light reflected itself on a string of yellow gourds hanging on the front of the chimney. It brightened the room.

Mrs. Wilkerson said, "Where I was raised, it was a

sin to burn a book." She turned to Phil and said, "Do
your people burn books?"

Phil felt uncomfortable over this criticism of Wilkerson.
He did not reply.

Wilkerson's voice sharpened. "Not *this* book," he
snapped. "This book is *Uncle Tom's Cabin*. It ought to
be burned. The writer—it's a woman—she's the worst
kind of troublemaker. Mouthy when she talks about
slavery. Stirrin' up hate. Yes, sir, stirrin' up hate for all
she's worth. There's already too much hate in the land.
What do you say, Mr. Sheridan?"

"I think you're right," Phil said slowly. "The slavery
I've seen isn't as bad as the way she writes it."

"Thank you," said Wilkerson.

Mrs. Wilkerson stood up, her eyes snapping. "Take
slavery here. Our nearest neighbors, the Jones. They live
ten miles down river. In December they sold a twelve-
year-old Negro girl away from her mother."

"How many other cases do you know like thet in your
lifetime?" Wilkerson asked his wife. "You don't know any.
I don't believe in selling children, but any nigger I ever
saw is better off a slave with white people taking care of
him than on his own. Some niggers is so lazy they wouldn't
throw a stick at a snake. To get work out of that kind, so
they'll earn their keep, they have to be treated tough.
And remember, the whites take care of 'em when they're
too old to do anything but eat."

"I don't know about that wonderful care you speak of,"
Mrs. Wilkerson said. Her voice had ice in it. "Slavery is
the biggest question facing the world today. Right now
up in Kansas and Nebraska emigrants are moving in so

when those territories vote on the question of being free or holding slaves, they'll—"

"It isn't votes that'll tell up there," Wilkerson interrupted. "It's Bowie knives, six-shooters, and whiskey. They need law. Slaves are worth millions. The Northerners hate the South because we own slaves. I'm not meanin' you, Mr. Sheridan. The best and the cheapest cowhand I ever owned was a nigger, and as soon as we get ahead— more cattle—I'm going to buy another."

"Not with me around you're not," Mrs. Wilkerson said.

"I want peace. I want it to remain in the land," Mr. Wilkerson said.

"I do, too," his wife replied.

There was a silence. The mesquite log looked as if it were fed by gas. Sparks sputtered onto the hearth. Wilkerson planted his boot on them hard enough to kill a turtle. He turned to Phil. "The big question will be settled by fightin'. What'll the Army do?"

"I don't know," Phil answered.

"I'll tell you what it'll do," Wilkerson drawled. "It'll split. Some will fight for the South, some for the North."

"I agree on that," said Mrs. Wilkerson. "Our country is going to be torn up just like you tore up that book."

"I'm for Texas and what's best for Texas," Wilkerson said. "This is my country. I fought Indians and renegades for it, and I'll fight Yankees if it comes down to that."

Phil's teamster interjected himself into the conversation. "A-men," he said.

Phil felt uncomfortable. He tried to change the subject. "Do you think the transcontinental railroad will go through?" he said.

"Never," said Wilkerson. "The Indians won't let it." He clapped on his hat. "I'm going out to check the horses."

Mrs. Wilkerson pointed a thumb at Phil. "His men are out there."

"Going out anyhow," Wilkerson said. "Need fresh air."

When Wilkerson returned, Mrs. Wilkerson went to bed. The rancher heaped more wood on the fire and sacrificed the rest of *Uncle Tom's Cabin*. He said to Phil, "You Yankees don't know our problems. President Pierce, New Hampshire man, he don't know 'em either. No one in the gov'ment knows."

"The Secretary of War's from the South," Phil said.

"Right. Jefferson Davis. Mississippi man. Mexican War background. The lieutenant colonel who commands Fort Duncan—what's his name—he fought in that war. Goes into a spasm if anyone mentions the Battle of Resaca de la Palma. Lost a thumb there."

Phil made a mental note not to mention the Battle of Resaca de la Palma at Fort Duncan.

When the time came to go to bed, Phil took his buffalo robe and lay down near the hearth. He thought a long time before he slept. There had been talk in the Army for years, he knew, about what would happen if civil war came. He had no idea the Southerners felt as strongly over slavery as Mr. Wilkerson. The slavery question seemed too big to be settled. "But it has to be settled," Phil whispered. He watched the fire for a long time, then went to sleep.

At daybreak Phil said good-bye to the Wilkersons. Mrs. Wilkerson gave him a lunch in a wicker basket.

"Fried chicken," she said. "I think there's enough for four."

"Come back and I'll get you a pony," Wilkerson said. "I'd be proud and happy."

The morning was pleasant and balmy, but the prairie looked as brown and as uninviting as it had all the way from the Gulf Coast. Even the mountains in the distance were unattractive. Phil unbuttoned the collar of his blue shirt and tucked up his sleeves. The wagon rolled over the rough track which seemed to stretch forever. The sun beat down. The air became oppressive. The mules lathered under their harness.

The driver said, "Sir, Lieutenant, unless I have my spurs tangled, we ought to hit Duncan about two this afternoon. These mules are the best pullers in Texas."

Being addressed in that fashion made Phil feel like a knight. "You handle 'em fine," he said.

The teamster sent his long whip over the mules with a crack. "Come on, you knobheads!" he shouted.

At two that afternoon the wagon toiled up a slope. Before them on the prairie squatted Fort Duncan. Phil's heart sank. Duncan looked as squalid as the Wilkerson ranch. Ten adobe buildings, and two built of logs, formed "Officers' Row." Three of the roofs were thatched. Adobe barracks were scattered about without plan. Some of the barracks had thatched sides. The teamster drove between two posts, where some joker had placed a sign reading GATE. There was no fence. The wind swept up a cloud of dust and hurled it across the moth-eaten parade ground. A tremor gripped Phil. He was afraid that the sight of his new home was making him ill.

The driver pointed at a log cabin that had a hogshead near one corner, situated so that it could catch rainwater from the roof. "That's headquarters. That's where you report in at."

Phil felt as he had when the river steamer, *New World*, brought him to West Point for the first time. He was anxious to make good. Another new world lay just ahead.

CHAPTER 7

Indian Country—Texas

THE teamster struggled into his leather coat. He pointed at a blue cloud sweeping up from the horizon. Dust engulfed the fort. You could hardly see across the parade ground. The light faded. "A blue norther," the teamster shouted. "Temperature'll drop sixty, seventy degrees in an hour."

The entire sky changed to deep blue. Phil shivered. "How long will this last?" he said.

"Three days—maybe four. You jump off. I'll hustle these mules to the stable. I'll get your baggage later."

The wind blew a gale, driving the rain in level sheets.

Phil knocked on the door of headquarters and opened it. An officer wearing a fringed buckskin shirt stood up. Sewed to the shirt's shoulders were epaulets designed for a full-dress blue uniform, and embroidered in silver on the epaulets were colonel's eagles. Two more silver eagles were pinned on the front tips of the buckskin collar. The colonel's pistol and its holster hung from his belt, which had a brass buckle six inches by four, reading U. S. ARMY.

On the front of his desk lay a saber, a black felt hat, and a pair of buckskin gloves.

Phil saluted. "Sir," he said, "Second Lieutenant Philip Sheridan reports for duty."

"For duty?" the colonel gasped. "Why, fine! I am Colonel Fowler, commanding." The colonel smoothed his handlebar mustache. "We're not expecting anyone. You precede your written orders. If you have a copy may I see them?"

Phil pulled a copy of his orders from his breast pocket. Colonel Fowler read them carefully. The wind hooted down the chimney.

"Splendid," the colonel said. "What's your background? Too young for the war, I see."

"Yes, sir. I just graduated from West Point last June, sir."

The colonel walked around his desk and shook hands with Phil, keeping his left hand behind his back. "Have a seat, Mister." He indicated a four-legged stool in front of the desk and pulled a straight-backed barrack chair out and sat beside Phil.

"Never served with a West Pointer before, except of course under the great ones in the Mexican War. This will be a pleasure. Did you have riding up at West Point, Mr. Sheridan?"

"Yes, sir."

"Fine. Splendid. Half the regiment's on horses. I say 'regiment' but don't let that mislead you. We have two companies only. The rest—scattered for miles. I want you to make yourself comfortable, then as soon as this norther blows itself out I'll send you out on patrol up to

La Pena, Camp La Pena. We have a half-company there. Yes, Mr. Sheridan, the officers here will welcome you heartily." The colonel chuckled as if he had made a joke. He fingered his mustache. "You'll be popular. The officers have had their fill of patrol duty. Where are you from?"

"Ohio, sir."

"Good. I'm from New York, myself. Just ten days ago we lost a topnotch man from my part of the country, Captain Michael VanBuren. Comanches got him. Van-Buren, he should have known better, a man of his war experience. He was on a patrol with twelve men. They ran across a pack of Comanches—some say twenty, some twenty-five. There's a board of officers investigating. Gallant old fellow, VanBuren. He attacked. An arrow struck him just above the sword belt. One private killed, another wounded—the shoulder. I don't question Captain VanBuren's tactics, no sir. Wouldn't criticize a dead man for the world, but get this in your head, Mr. Sheridan, we are not that good."

Phil gulped. "Yes, sir." The whole thing seemed a puzzle. What should Captain VanBuren have done?

"These Indians are tough," the colonel said. He toyed with a fringe on the sleeve of his jacket, then tucked his blue trousers deeper into his black boots. Phil decided to get a buckskin jacket like the colonel's.

"After they killed the captain and the scout of the first squad, Private Cain, they lit out for the Staked Plains in West Texas. They've a stronghold there." The colonel paused. "Where's your baggage?"

"Sir, the teamster has it."

The colonel blew his nose with a red bandana. "We have a vacant set of quarters, such as it is, down at the end of the row," the colonel said. "It's yours. When this norther is exhausted I want you to take one man and go on patrol to . . . "

One man!

The colonel grinned. "I know what you are thinking, Mr. Sheridan. Yes, one man. Learn this, sir. We are not sending out fighting patrols. The Indians do not realize it, but we want to avoid fights. Licking all the Indians in Texas would take—well, it's impossible. You scout to our post at La Pena and return. Take two weeks going and two more returning. It's only ninety miles, but I want you to learn the country. Get familiar with it. If you see Indians up to eight, you ride like the devil for the closest post fast and report."

"Yes, sir."

"Orderly!" the colonel shouted.

A soldier wearing blue trousers tucked into canvas leggings, a red woolen shirt, and leather belt supporting a bayonet, hurried from behind a partition and stood at attention before the colonel. The colonel caught Phil's eyes on the soldier's red shirt. "Informal out here," the colonel said. "We get inspected once a year from San Antone. We save our uniforms for that inspection." He turned to the soldier. "Take Mr. Sheridan to the vacant set of quarters. Sweep it out and make him comfortable. Get his baggage."

"Yes, sir." The orderly saluted.

"Mr. Sheridan, Mrs. Fowler and I will expect you at our quarters for dinner at six."

For the next two days, while the blue norther exhausted itself, Phil and the old soldier assigned to scout with him, Private Frankman, readied their equipment. Frankman was a Texan. He had "cut meat" in a San Antonio butcher shop before joining the Army. He was a sportsman and hunter, and his knowledge of the Rio Grande country earned him almost constant patrol duty. He was dressed in buckskins, deerskin moccasins, trousers, and shirt. They were almost black.

Frankman left nothing to chance. He examined every strap of their equipment and each round of ammunition. "You think I'm an old lady," he said to Phil. "I take chances after I leave, not before."

The soldier took Phil to the blacksmith shop, where he had the pack mule they were to use, and instructed Phil in how to throw the diamond hitch.

"Ain't nothing worse," Frankman cautioned, "than being on the trail and have your dern jughead strew your belongings and fixin's about. This mule is standin' docile as a lamb with his blinders on, but he knows what we're doing, and he'd try to undo it on the march. Once I saw a man try to hypnotize a jarhead when they were packin' him, so he wouldn't know he was being loaded, but it didn't work. Nothing smarter than a mule."

"How many patrols have you been on?" Phil asked.

"Too many to count, Lieutenant," Frankman said, "but they haven't raised my scalp yet, and I don't intend fer 'em to. You take that rattle Cap'n VanBuren got into. If it had been me I'd have known what to do. About five years ago I was on a scout along Devils River. It swarmed

Indians and we turned tail and galloped. That's why
I'm here."

Phil wished he had experiences he could discuss with
Frankman, but he kept quiet. The instruction in patrolling
on horseback at West Point seemed too tame to talk about.

Frankman held up a small shotgun. "This is the prin-
ciplest thing to take. This and shells. 'Cause quails taste
wonderful roasted on a sage stick. Sir, I am confidentially
worried over that hoss you're going to ride."

"Why?"

"The first sergeant—I don't want to butt in on his
business, but he's going to assign you Great Smoky. That
hoss has a fence rail for a backbone and a mouth of iron
that'll pull your arms out. Are you any good at politics,
sir? You should be on Georgia. Good gaits and can run.
This isn't giggle talk, sir. I'd regret to see you on Great
Smoky. I hope you kin work it." Frankman half-covered
his mouth with the palm of his hand and lowered his voice.
"The first sergeant keeps Georgia for his own *in case* he
has to ride, but he only mounts up onct in a blue moon."

When the storm blew over, Phil and Frankman rode
away from the post. Frankman led the pack mule. Phil
was mounted on Georgia. The first sergeant had been easy
to persuade, because Phil flattered him by asking his advice
on a number of matters.

Phil turned in his saddle and looked back. He was
glad to get away from the post. Already Fort Duncan
was a low blur on the prairie. Only the flag flying from
the pole gave it distinction.

Private Frankman rode according to custom, two paces
to the left and three to the rear.

"Come up with me, Frankman," Phil said, then added, "I want to thank you for all you did to get us ready."

"It's my pleasure," said Frankman, jerking the rope leading to the halter of the pack mule.

A senior never thanks a junior for doing his duty, Phil remembered. Then, as if to kill a silly custom, Phil thanked Frankman all over again.

Three miles farther, Frankman pointed to a small knoll. "I saw an Indian over there." Phil's mouth went dry. In a minute a lone Indian trotted up. The Comanche sat bareback on a calico pony. He had one rein, a thong to the animal's muzzle. He gripped a bow and arrows in the other hand. In his belt was a wicked-looking knife.

The Indian stopped his pony and spouted a stream of gibberish. Even though Phil could not understand, he knew what the Indian wanted. He was asking for a present.

"Don't give him anything, is my special advice," Frankman said. "They always want somethin' and never even thank you."

Phil shook his head and the Indian rode away on a different tack than the one Phil and Frankman were taking.

Phil thought over the first wild Indian he had seen. "I can't get over the idea he had no saddle, no nothing," he said.

"That's what makes them so hard to catch and beat, sir. We hang everything but a kitchen stove and a Christmas tree on our saddles. The Indian—" Frankman shrugged his shoulders, "he's bothered by nothin' but his weapons."

The warm April sun made the prairie beautiful. Gone was its drab appearance. The sun and rain had brought out earth smells. Phil felt as if he were riding in a garden. Ahead a large area was tinted blue. "Buffalo clover," Frankman explained. "Over there, that purple splotch with the green bottom is thistle sage. Pretty, I say."

A mile farther Frankman said, "Sir, excuse me for making a suggestion. Ordinarily I don't go direct, but I go through channels." He laughed.

Phil grinned. He liked Frankman.

The soldier continued, "Only here there aren't any channels. It's just us, the two horses, and the jarhead. Let's go military, sir. Let me be the point and ride out ahead. I can take care of you up in front if anything turns up."

Phil felt he had known Private Frankman all his life. *And I'll take care of you, Frankman,* he said to himself.

The two friends scouted for Indians all morning, then hunted quail. At nightfall Frankman pointed to a small arroyo where they could build a campfire unobserved. They had more quail than they could eat. "We'll save some for breakfast," Frankman said. "Sir, tomorrow I guarantee you venison. We don't have to worry about Indians. The colonel says, 'Find 'em,' but watch, sir, they won't corroberate. After that killing, Indians will be scarce."

"Tell me about the Indians," Phil said. "What do they think? What are their habits?"

"It's like this, Mr. Sheridan. They're confused. We made a treaty with 'em after our war with Mexico. The Indians thought then they could raid the Mexicans any time they wanted. When we stopped that they turned on us. Now they hang out mostly in the Staked Plains, miles from here. But if they ever go off half-cocked and pull the Army out of here, look out."

For the next sixteen months Phil and Frankman rode on scout after scout. The Indians scarcely appeared. They avoided the Army. The Texas Rangers fought parties of Comanches and Lipans, but the Army had little contact with the warlike tribes. Once the Comanches sneaked up on the fort and killed a drummer boy within sight of the flagpole. Colonel Fowler alerted every man, and his soldiers chased the raiders back to their stronghold in the Staked Plains. The Army stopped there, for the Staked Plains were true Indian territory. "It would be foolish to go in there and fight," the colonel said. "We'd have to have the whole United States Army."

As a hobby, Phil studied the birds and hunted with Frankman. Together they supplied the post with venison. Phil avoided parties. Once, when an officer's wife invited him to her home, Phil replied that he could not come because he had scheduled a hunt, but that he would send back venison and quail.

Phil thought of himself as a fixture at Fort Duncan until one day in 1855 when the colonel sent for him. Phil stood before the desk wondering what he had done wrong.

"Phil," the colonel said, "the adjutant has your orders for the Fourth Infantry in Oregon Territory."

Oregon! It seemed a million miles away.

"I hate to see you go," the colonel said. "You've done fine work. There's excitement ahead for you. It's my guess that out there you'll smell gunpowder. You're a salute and shoot soldier. You'll do all right."

It was hard for Phil to tell his friend Frankman good-bye. Phil stammered when he shook the private soldier's hand. Phil had little to say.

Frankman broke the silence. "Mr. Sheridan, I hate to tell you good-bye, but there'll be fellows like me taking care of you always. You are going to see a heap of soldiers in your time."

CHAPTER 8

Trip to Oregon

I̶T WAS dangerous for a man to travel overland alone from Texas to Oregon Territory. So, instead of a trip of a thousand miles, Phil made one of ten thousand. He went to New Orleans, up the Mississippi River to Cincinnati, to his home at Somerset for a few days, to New York City, down the Atlantic Coast, through the Caribbean Sea to Panama, across the Isthmus, up the Pacific Coast to San Francisco, and overland to Oregon.

The first stage was the most tiresome, back over the lonely prairie miles to Corpus Christi, Texas. There was a wait for a ship to take him to New Orleans, and when it came the captain had startling news. "Awful time up in Kansas," the skipper said. "Five thousand border ruffians poured across the Missouri and forced 'em to rig up a pro-slavery government for Kansas Territory. A lot of killin'. I want peace, personally. Most people do."

The world seemed upside down. Phil was glad he was going to Oregon. Maybe there he'd be free from the slavery question.

In New York Harbor Phil faced a problem of his own. When he reported to Governors Island the colonel said, "Mr. Sheridan, I have a job for you. Over on Bedloe's Island we have three hundred recruits. A bad lot. Very unruly. Now take that as a warning. You get them ready to sail for Panama and the West Coast. Best thing to do is to handle 'em sternly. If you wish to court-martial the ringleaders, I'll back you up. That may be the solution— court-martial."

Phil's recruits were sullen. They had been in the Army only a short time but they hated it. They were ready for mutiny. "We ain't going to do a damned thing you say," one recruit told Phil. "Not a thing."

"What's the matter?" Phil asked.

"Well, if we are in the Army," the soldier replied, "why don't they give us uniforms and food we can eat?"

Phil investigated, then took the small boat back to Governors Island. He went to the colonel and demanded uniforms and decent rations for the recruits.

"This isn't the way I'd solve it," the colonel growled. "Why don't you get them in order first?"

But Phil stood his ground stubbornly, and the colonel did as Phil asked.

Back at Bedloe's Island, Phil made the recruits clean up. He taught them drill. When the huge sailing vessel anchored off Bedloe's two months later, Phil's three hundred men looked and acted like soldiers. Phil was happy when he boarded the ship and turned the recruits over to a first lieutenant who was to command them on the trip to the West Coast.

When the ship's anchor rattled to the bottom off the

Panamanian coast after thirteen days at sea, Phil got his first close-up of the tropics. It was interesting. Palms and mangrove trees bordered the beach. In the distance blue-green hills rose, covered with jungle. They looked unreal —like stage scenery. Phil had never been hotter. Every soul on board sought shade. The sails hung motionless in the rigging. The ship rolled gently in the long swell.

A white man, tanned by the tropical sun, paddled out in a dugout canoe. He climbed a rope ladder and, when he was on deck, he bowed to the captain, to the first lieutenant, and to Phil. *"Buenas días, señors,"* the man said. "Good day. I am your guide through the jungle. I am hired by the Army of your country to get you and your men to Panama City. I have a hundred and ten ponies and fifty natives at your service." The man flashed his white teeth in a smile and bowed.

"How many miles is it across?" Phil asked.

The guide shrugged. "It is up and down jungle trails, around a lake. Forty-seven, fifty, fifty-five, sixty, sixty-five."

He sounds like an auctioneer, Phil thought.

The first lieutenant said, "How about that railroad they're building? Any chance of riding that even part of the way?"

"Come later this year, *señor*. Maybe then."

"Is there a ship waiting for us on the other side?" Phil asked.

"I do not know, *señor*. It has been ten days since I was in Panama City. They come and go." The guide raised his hands.

"You haven't enough ponies for us all to ride," the first lieutenant said. "What do we do, take turns?"

"Certainly, *señor*, except for the *jefes*." The guide looked at Phil and the first lieutenant. "For you, I have two magnificent horses."

"I would just as soon take my turn walking," Phil said. Perspiration streamed down his forehead. He wished he was dressed as comfortably as the guide, who wore white trousers, a white shirt open at the throat, a wide straw hat, and boots. The blue woolen Army uniforms were suffocating.

It was a relief to leave the ship, but after Phil had been in the jungle an hour he wished he were back on board. Hordes of mosquitoes attacked. When the column rested, bugs of every kind bit the travelers. The native grooms did not seem to mind the insects; the Spanish guide wore headnet and gloves. The Las Cruces trail was muddy because the sun could not get through the jungle. The ponies were wretched—bones and skin—the worst Phil had ever seen.

The trail, seven feet wide, wound through the dense growth. Part of it was paved with moss-covered stones. The Spaniard pointed at the flagstones and said, "Long ago the pirate Morgan made his slaves lay these when he crossed the Isthmus to steal gold from Panama City. Magnificent robber."

The heat became almost unbearable. The jungle stank. There seemed to be no air. The North Americans perspired through their uniforms. At night, in camp along the trail, the soldiers tried to light fires to smoke away the insects, but the rotten jungle wood was too wet to burn. Phil wanted water. A horseholder took a long-bladed *machete* from his belt and sliced a heavy vine hanging from a tree. Water trickled out of the vine. It tasted wooden, but it was fresh. Phil and men nearby filled their canteens.

Suddenly lightning split the sky. The rain poured in torrents, and the trail flooded. When daylight came every native was gone. The guide cursed in Spanish. He explained, "The stupid grooms took the rain in the dry season as a sign of evil."

The column pushed on, slower now because the grooms and horseholders had deserted.

When the caravan walked and rode into Panama City, Phil was tired, dirty, and hot. Huge cumulus clouds crowned a mountain range in the distance. Four sailing ships rode the blue water of the bay. Graceful frigate birds sailed about the ships and over the white adobe buildings of the city. An arrow of awkward pelicans flew by on a fishing trip to one of the offshore islands.

It required half a day to make arrangements for the party to sail for San Francisco. When they were finally underway, the cool ocean breeze was a reprieve. The creak of the ship and the wind rushing through the cordage was music.

Phil liked the captain because he gave Phil the courtesy of the bridge. It was thrilling to stand and watch the bow cleave the water and to see, every once in a while, a wave crash headlong into the bow. You could feel the ship tremble. Spray would be thrown almost as far as the bridge. On the fourth day Phil was on the bridge when the lookout reported a sail. The skipper reached for a spyglass and, after a few minutes, said, "Take the glass, Mr. Sheridan. Clipper ship coming. You can make out the tips of her three masts. I think she's the *Flying Cloud*. Record holder, sir. Eighty-nine days from New York to San Francisco. You won't see many more clippers. They need freight space now, that's what they require, because the gold rush fever is cooling off."

The sleek-looking clipper ship broke out a signal. "She has a message for us," the skipper said.

It made Phil dizzy to watch sailors on both ships scramble out on the yardarms, high above the decks, and reef in canvas. Shortly, the two ships lay parallel, a hundred yards apart, rolling in the trough of the waves.

A rowboat pulled away from the *Flying Cloud*. The oars glistened in the sun as the little boat fought the waves. When it bounced alongside the transport, the officer in the rowboat handed up six melons, a letter, and a packet of newspapers. He cupped his hands about his mouth and shouted, "Please deliver this letter to our agent in San Francisco."

In ten minutes the rowboat was back aboard the clipper and the two ships were underway. In thirty, they were out of sight of each other.

The captain invited Phil to his cabin to eat melons and to read the *Sacramento Union*. The front page of the paper was covered with announcements of arrivals and departures of ships. The second told of the fine work of the Vigilance Committee in San Francisco in trying to rid the city of thieves, murderers, and crooked politicians. Page three described the fierce struggle in Kansas Territory over slavery. And tucked away on the last page was an article which made Phil jump.

TROUBLE OVER GOLD
ARMY TO CHECK PROPOSED LAYOUT OF R.R. FROM SACRAMENTO TO COLUMBIA
— o —
Indians Paint Up

A despatch from Oregon Territory tells of Indians on the warpath. The Governor treated with the tribes for land near the Columbia River, but miners pouring into the Territory are not interested in the treaty. The Indians are angry because mining operations kill the fish. Two miners scalped last week.

In the month, Lieut. R. S. Williamson, U. S. Army Topographical Engineer, will lead a surveying party through the area to discover a route for a railroad from the Sacramento River to the Columbia River. Soldiers under Lts. George Crook and John Hood, 4th U. S. Infantry, will guard the engineer's party.

Phil bounced to his feet. He read the article out loud. "Crook and Hood are my friends," he said excitedly. "The Fourth Infantry, that's the outfit I'm going to."

"Looks like you're heading into a mess," the captain said.

Phil read and reread the article. He wished it had more details.

It was dusk when the ship slipped through the Golden Gate. The cloud effect was magnificent. The last rays of the sun made the tops of the hills on both sides golden brown. Lights twinkled in San Francisco and dotted the far eastern shore. In the southern part of the bay you could see the dark hulls of ships at anchor. "Probably grain ships," the captain said.

The ship sailed between Bird Rock and Alcatraz and tacked northward up the bay. At nine the anchor chain roared, signaling the end of the long voyage. "We are off the Navy Yard," the skipper said. "We'll ease up the channel to Benicia early in the morning."

Phil thanked the captain. It was a happy moment. Phil looked forward to leaving the ship and to adventures in Oregon Territory. Down in his cabin he repacked his trunk. His buckskin shirt, lying on top, made him think of Texas. It seemed half the world away. He remembered Colonel Fowler's prediction: *You will smell powder in Oregon.* Phil oiled his pistol, then took his sword down to the ship's carpenter to be sharpened.

The carpenter eased his thumb along the blade. "This isn't dull," he said. "You must be 'spectin' trouble."

CHAPTER 9

Indian Country—Oregon

THE lieutenant colonel at Benicia Barracks stroked his beard and told Phil of his trip across country years ago with pioneers. He made Phil think of Captain Brewerton, the West Point Superintendent.

After a while the old officer stepped to a map of California and Oregon on the wall. Phil was intensely interested. The colonel placed a finger at Fort Reading, far to the north near Shasta Lake, California. "Mr. Sheridan, you are to report at Reading and relieve Mr. Hood as guard on a surveying party. Forty dragoons he's commanding. You'll travel up the Sacramento, but it is quite a jaunt alone in the saddle. Too far. A week from today we have six escort wagons going up there freighting supplies. You go with them."

Phil thought of seven days in Benicia with nothing to do. He wanted action. It would be exciting to command forty dragoons after sixteen months in Texas commanding just Private Frankman.

"Where are the Indians?" Phil asked.

"Indians? Oh, they're out from Reading." The colonel swept his palm over the area northeast of Mount Lassen and over the Columbia River country.

"Sir, if you can furnish me with a horse I'd like to start now. I don't mind riding alone."

"*Harumph!*" the colonel snorted. "Supposing you have an accident? On the trail all by yourself, and I approved it. Not a good idea. I'd be held responsible."

"Sir, this is civilized country, isn't it?"

"Well, I—yes, I suppose it is."

"Sir, please let me go."

The colonel thought the matter over a long time—a half hour, it seemed to Phil. "Two hundred and fifty miles alone," the colonel said. "You are taking a chance. If you were thrown from your horse . . . Well, it's your party. Get yourself gone. The stable sergeant will give you a horse. Tell him I said to."

It was pleasant riding along the tree-bordered banks of the Sacramento. Phil trotted by boatmen working to get heavily laden scows upstream. He passed miners and pack trains heading for mining country. At one place two men worked to dig an irrigation ditch to turn water into a newly plowed field. Phil galloped by three "Last Chance" saloons. On the third day, a canoe shot around the bend, making time with the current. Paddling in the stern sat an Indian wearing a wolf-skin vest and a plug hat ornamented with a red feather. Down in the bow, his feet over the gunwales, sat a miner with a jug in his lap. The miner was dirty and happy. "Hey, boy!" he shouted at Phil. "Turn that cayuse around and head back to Sacramento. I'll show you a good time. Struck it rich!"

Phil waved and trotted on upstream. At noon on the fifth day he rode into Fort Reading. The fort had thick walls of adobe, but small buildings clustered about it would mask much of the fire from defenders. It was a disappointment.

Phil reported to a fat major who commanded the tiny fort. The major sat in a rocking chair behind a pine desk. He did not bother to get up when Phil saluted, but stopped rocking and put out his hand. Phil stood at attention while the major talked.

"Too bad, Mr. Sheridan. The Williamson bunch left here five days ago. Quite an expedition. Smart fellow, Mr. Williamson. All those Topographical Engineers are, and don't think they don't know it. Let me see your orders, young fellow. Why weren't you here on time? You were supposed to have relieved Mr. Hood and taken over the forty dragoons he commands."

The major pored carefully over each indorsement of Phil's orders—the notes made by commanding officers along the route. Phil ran a finger around the inside of the collar of his blue woolen shirt.

The major passed the orders back to Phil. "You made remarkable good time," he said. "It's not your fault you missed the surveying party. You stick around. I'll find something for you to do. Too late to go now. How are you on infantry drill?" The major leaned back in his rocking chair, scratched his head, and looked up at Phil.

"Sir, I want to start after Mr. Williamson. I can catch

a big party like that. He'll have to make camp whenever he stops to survey. He's surveying for a railroad, isn't he?"

The major began rocking. In a moment he said, "You rode by yourself up the Sacramento River, but it ain't the same headin' into the wild country of the Pitt Rivers."

"The Pitt Rivers?"

"Indians!" The major shouted the word. He jumped out of the chair. "Cruelest bunch on the continent. Why, if they caught you, no telling what they'd do. Unspeakable. They gobble up parties under a dozen just like that." The major snapped his fingers. "Mr. Sheridan, out in that wild mountainous country the advantage is all on the side of the Indians. They'd cut off the soles of your feet and burn you upside down at the stake. I cannot spare fifteen men to ride with you—that's a minimum. Mr. Williamson has a hundred—forty of Mr. Hood's dragoons, and sixty foot soldiers under Mr. Crook."

"Sir, if you'd please give me one or two men I'll go. If anything happens, I will write a paper now so you won't be to blame." Phil's lustrous eyes blazed at the major.

"Great Scott, Sheridan!" The major stamped up and down the narrow office. "You don't begin to know the situation. The Pitt Rivers are controlling the wild country. The Rogue River Indians have attacked pioneers up in Oregon and have gotten away with it. This encouraged the Pitts and all the rest. The Rogues and the Pitts especially have been murdering, robbing pack trains, committing all the crimes in the book—and you can throw in more. They're fighting along the Columbia, too. The Oregon people have armed every boy over twelve with

View of West Point just prior to the Civil War

Lieutenant George W. Crook, Cadet Phil Sheridan, and Lieutenant John Nugent, 1852

Lost Dispatches

Photographs top and bottom:
Courtesy of Library of Congress;
left: Century Magazine, 1890—
Harvard College Library; right:
Living History, Inc.

ABOVE: The Patient Pack-
mule, *by Frederic Rem-
ington*

RIGHT: Mounted Indian,
by Frederic Remington

HARPER'S WEEKLY.

A JOURNAL OF CIVILIZATION.

Vol. V.—No. 227.]   NEW YORK, SATURDAY, MAY 4, 1861.   [SINGLE COPIES SIX CENTS.
[$2 50 PER YEAR IN ADVANCE.

Entered according to Act of Congress, in the Year 1861, by Harper & Brothers, in the Clerk's Office of the District Court for the Southern District of New York.

THE HOUSE-TOPS IN CHARLESTON DURING THE BOMBARDMENT OF SUMTER.

The First Virginia Cavalry, one of the crack regiments of the Civil War, *by Alfred R. Waud*

Photographs right and below: Courtesy of Library of Congress

Lincoln reviewing the cavalry of the Army of the Potomac, April 9, 1863, *by Alfred R. Waud*

Sheridan and his staff

U.S. Signal Corps photo

TOP: Attack on Union Supply Train near Jasper, Tennessee, *by J. F. E. Hillen.* CENTER: Battle of Chickamauga, *by J. F. E. Hillen.* BOTTOM: The Courier, *by Gilbert Gaul.*

TOP: Sheridan's wagon trains. LEFT: Hospital attendants collecting the wounded at night after the battle, *by William Waud*. BOTTOM: A Richmond and Fredericksburg railroad bridge over the North Anna, set afire by Sheridan's Raiders, *by Alfred R. Waud*.

Photograph by courtesy of W. H. Carter, Sixth Cavalry, Harvard College Library

TOP: Captured by Mosby's Guerrillas. LEFT: Colonel John S. Mosby, 43rd Battalion, Virginia Cavalry. BOTTOM: 7th New York Heavy Artillery at Cold Harbor, June 3, 1864, *by Alfred R. Waud.*

Photograph left: L. C. Handy Studios; Brady-Handy Collection, Library of Congress; permission of Mrs. Alice Cox. Below: Library of Congress

Photographs by courtesy of Library of Congress

TOP: Pontoon bridge above Jones's Landing on the James River. BOTTOM: General Lee leaving the McLean House after the surrender, April 9, 1865, *by Alfred R. Waud.*

a rifle. That's the country our topographical friend is heading into. And you want to—My heavens, man!"

Phil said quietly, "Sir, I want to go. I am willing to take a chance."

The major reluctantly gave Phil a corporal, old enough to be his father, and two privates. The horses were the fastest in the fort.

Before Phil went to the stable to inspect the three mounted men the major said, "Mr. Sheridan, these are the best men I have. Corporal Lamerick knows this country. Raised in it. The two privates are sharpshooters. I tell you this, you'd better ride like hell and catch Mr. Williamson before the Pitt River tribe catches you. We can spare you, but not Corporal Lamerick and the two sharpshooters."

Phil was so happy to be released for the trip he overlooked the insult. He said to himself, *We can travel faster than Frankman and I used to—no pack mule.*

When Phil completed his inspection of the corporal, the two men, the saddle rolls, the horses, the arms and ammunition, he stood again before the major in headquarters. The major pushed himself out of his rocking chair and waggled a finger at Phil. "Remember, Mr. Sheridan, all you have is a little hardtack and coffee. You have to catch Mr. Williamson in three days at the outside. If you don't—starvation." The major's piglike eyes bulged. "I'm letting you take a chance. Why, I don't know. I wish you luck. I'll come outside and see you off."

Phil stood to horse in front of the three troopers. It was a bright July day. When the major approached, Phil touched the rim of his black hat smartly. When the major returned the salute, Phil turned his head and commanded, "Prepare to mount. *Mount!*"

The three cavalrymen climbed into their saddles. Phil grabbed the saddlehorn of his mount and swung to the animal's back. He tickled the horse with a spur and the stallion whirled about, dancing, stirring up the dust. The long fringe on Phil's buckskin shirt spun out. Phil motioned toward the east, and the party galloped down the dirt road toward the wild Mount Lassen volcano country. Phil Sheridan was taking a chance, but he was confident he would succeed. The air rushing by his face felt good.

Two miles from the fort, in a lare cut through a forest of pines and yellow-green oaks, Phil stopped the group. "Corporal Lamerick," he said, "send one man forward two hundred yards as a point. And the other man, let him be the rear guard a hundred yards back. You ride with me. I'll set the pace."

When the party forded Cow Creek, the trail led through a primeval forest. Every so often, from a clearing, you could see a tall cinder cone and back of it the majestic, snow-covered Mount Lassen. The mountain dominated the country.

The trail of the Williamson party was easy to follow along creek bottoms and around blue-tinted lakes because its supply wagons churned a road. Even when the wagons rolled over volcanic rock they left telltale scratches.

"Just like I predicted," Corporal Lamerick said. "Sir, he's headin' northwest, skirtin' the Chaos Crags which got pushed up when the volcano mountain exploded about two hundred years ago. It's slightly impossible for a body to believe everything he hears about this country, but even a skim milk cowboy can tell that the Chaos Crags and Jumbles were put there by the old volcano."

"How far ahead do you think they are?" Phil asked.

"Couldn't say."

At dusk, on the banks of a stream that talked its way over countless boulders through a forest, the trooper in front signaled with his palm up, "Friends in sight."

Phil spurred his pony forward. In a clearing squatted a log cabin. Thin blue smoke rose from its chimney. "Someone inside," the trooper said to Phil.

When Phil rode to the cabin door a soldier with a complexion the color of chalk scrambled to his feet. Phil thought at first he was a deserter.

"Private Joseph Henry, sir, of Mr. Hood's dragoons," the soldier said. "Mr. Hood left me here two days ago with the miner who owns this cabin. I had stomach trouble. I guess they figgered I was about to die."

When the soldier learned that Phil was trailing the Williamson party, he begged to go along. "I'm a hundred per cent better, sir. Please don't leave me here. I tell you this, an extra man won't do you no harm."

"I know this man," said Corporal Lamerick. "Good man. If we have a corpse and cartridge occasion with any of these Pitt River Indians, his gun will come in mighty handy. I recommend, take him."

But in the middle of the next morning Private Henry fell off his horse. He held his stomach and rolled in the trail grass. The party dismounted and stood beside the stricken man. What to do? "I can't go on," the sick man moaned. "Don't leave me. I'll never make it back. My side!"

Phil asked Corporal Lamerick what he advised. Each man of the party answered, and each had a different idea. "I think we all ought to turn back," one soldier said.

Phil thought the matter over. He could not leave the soldier alone in the wilderness. If he became better, one man might be able to help him back to Fort Reading. Phil left one soldier with the sick man, and the party trotted ahead. Phil was not happy. Instead of being strengthened, his party was weakened.

Just after the noon halt to graze the horses and to eat hardtack, Phil found a yellow arrow in the trail. It was only eighteen inches long. Its feathers were worn, but its flint point was sharp. He could sense the anxiety of the two soldiers. He questioned himself, *Am I leading these two men to their deaths?*

"Let's tighten the girths," he said. "It's no time to quit now. Corporal, how far ahead do you think the surveying party is?"

"Sir, I can't say. Truth is, I thought we'd catch 'em afore now. Lieutenant Williamson is doin' dern little surveyin'."

The next afternoon at four the corporal, riding in front, held up his rifle and signaled, "Enemy in sight!" He threw himself off his horse.

Phil's heart jumped. He rode carefully up to the soldier, who led his horse back down the trail to meet him.

"Indians just ahead," the corporal whispered. "About a hundred yards. And about five hundred yards in front

of them is the surveying party. The Indians are trailin'
'em."

"How many Indians do you think there are?" Phil
asked. His voice quivered from excitement.

"About fifty, the ones I saw. They're Pitt Rivers, I
think."

From the looks of the moccasin tracks in the dirt at
his feet, Phil estimated there were a hundred Indians
ahead.

"How are we going to get to the surveying party?"
Phil asked.

"I dunno," the corporal replied.

CHAPTER 10

"I Will Not Give Up This Fort"

PHIL yanked his field glasses from their little leather case and focused on the Indians. By his side stood his two men. The three horses were tied in a grove to the rear.

The floor of the narrow valley ahead was hard, flinty lava, but its slopes were fertile. They were bright with California poppies, lacy green Dutchman's breeches, white goat's beard, golden marsh marigold, and Pitt River Indians. It seemed strange that death could be in a garden of flowers. Phil's hands trembled.

Ahead a half mile lumbered the surveyor's wagon train. Its rear guard was unaware it was followed by Indians. The field glasses brought the Indians up close.

Even though the Indians were a hundred yards away, he whispered to the two men, "About thirty. They have bows and arrows. How are we going to get to the train?" His black eyebrows came together. He motioned the two men back behind a thick rhododendron bush.

"This is a council of war," Phil said. "Speak your minds. I think we can take a chance. We can swing out to the right, out of the range of their arrows, and dash for the train. What do you think?"

The corporal swallowed. He shook his head. "Holy mackerel! Supposing there are Indians in the valley we don't see?"

The private said, "I'm with the lieutenant. We can skin by them before they know what's up."

Phil patted his empty saddlebag. "I have three pieces of hardtack left. You don't have any. This is our emergency ration. It would be a hard ride back to Reading. We can't go back. Corporal Lamerick, are you willing to follow me?"

The corporal nodded and inspected the load in his pistol.

The private said, "I am, sir."

"Bring up the horses," Phil said.

It was a tense moment. The three men tightened their saddle girths. They shook hands. "I'll go first," Phil said. "If we run into Indians we don't see, or anything unexpected, do as I do."

Phil led the dash along the right slope of the knifelike valley through a field of yellow poppies. The wind tore at his face. His dark eyes watered from excitement. It was hard to see. The hoofs of the horses pounded a frantic tattoo. Phil bent low. He gripped his horse with his knees as hard as he could. He prayed no horse would stumble. Out of the corner of his eye he saw the Indians were watching but were not following. Some were walking their ponies over the lava beds.

Suddenly Phil saw why the Indians were letting the three riders alone. Dead ahead was a wide creek with steep slopes. No horse could get across. On the creek bank, Phil wheeled his horse. The animal reared. The two soldiers just behind reined in their mounts. Froth from his heavily breathing stallion flew into Phil's face. Phil fired his pistol into the air four times.

"Trapped," said the corporal.

The private dismounted and prepared to fight.

Phil stood in his stirrups. The rear guard of the train stopped. In a moment, horsemen from the train rode back toward the three men, but slowly. Phil reloaded his pistol. His hands trembled.

"Here come the Indians," said the corporal. He turned his horse loose and threw himself down behind a bush.

Phil sat on his horse. The pounding of his heart seemed almost as loud as the breathing of the animal.

Six Indians rode their ponies up within forty yards. One Indian raised his arm, palm up. Phil returned the signal. The Indians walked their horses slowly up to Phil. He stopped them ten yards away. One Indian said something in Pitt River talk. When he finished, he patted his stomach.

"He says they are hungry," the corporal said to Phil. "That the miners hunting for gold have poisoned the streams. That the fish have died. Now all they have to eat is grasshoppers."

"From the looks of 'em," Phil said, "I think they are telling the truth."

The rest of the Indians came up. One waded into the stream fifty yards away to show Phil where the ford was. He pointed at a dip in the banks.

On the other side, shortly, Second Lieutenant George

Crook rode up with four soldiers. Phil dismounted and shook his friend's hand. "I was glad to see you when you waited for me when you graduated," Phil said, "but you don't know how glad I am to see you now."

Phil reported to Lieutenant Williamson. Williamson, a tall, serious-looking man, shook hands gravely. "I admire you for joining us," he said. "Just a moment." The leader of the expedition gave orders for the wagons to be drawn up in a circle and camp to be pitched. Shortly the woods echoed the sound of axes biting wood so that tents could have poles and the cooks firewood.

Mr. Williamson said to Phil, "Let's have a look at your Indians."

When the thirty Pitt River Indians faced them, carefully guarded, the engineer said, "Sad-looking bunch—very. Stomachs stuck out in hunger. They look like they told your interpreter the truth—been eating grasshoppers." The breeze bore the scent of beef stew from a cook's portable oven and the Indians dashed for the kitchen, followed by the guards.

While the Indians were gorging themselves on beef stew and coffee, Second Lieutenant John Hood, just off patrol, rode up. The husky blond swung out of the saddle. He was dressed in buckskins so trail-worn they were black. Even in moccasins he towered a foot over Phil. Hood's eyes, unusually deep in their sockets, smiled. He put out his hand and Phil shook it. "Never expected to see you after we left the fort," Hood said. "Welcome."

Mr. Hood paraded his forty dragoons for Phil's inspection. They were veterans, most of them frontiersmen. Then the tall Kentuckian said to Phil, "I'll leave first thing in the morning for the fort with the two men you brought. I hope I don't have a close escape, as you did."

Before Hood left for his assignment he drawled, "Phil, what's the news on the outside?"

"They're having the devil's own time in Kansas over the slavery problem," Phil answered.

"Many people have the wrong idea of slavery," the Kentuckian said. "The Bible itself approves of it. My folks own slaves, and they aim to keep on owning them." Hood was preaching gospel which he believed and would fight for.

Mr. Williamson beckoned to Phil. They walked up on the hillside above the camp, almost to the line of outguards. The camp in the valley looked wonderful.

"When you were cut off by the stream you had a narrow escape," Mr. Williamson said. "Ordinarily those Indians are worse than dynamite, but fortunately for you they were starving. They figured that by helping you and your two men they would be rewarded with food. If they hadn't been so hungry they would have wiped you out. Your gamble was lucky, I'm glad to say."

"It was a tough situation," Phil said. "We were out of food."

"I know, but when you take a chance, Sheridan, take a good look at every possible thing before you make the plunge. In war it's a good idea to take a chance when you are sure it'll succeed. Being smart in taking your chances is different than recklessness. I'm not up here to lecture you, but to tell you what I'm doing, and I want to give you your job." Williamson spoke quietly. Phil liked him.

"I'm not much older than you are," Williamson con-

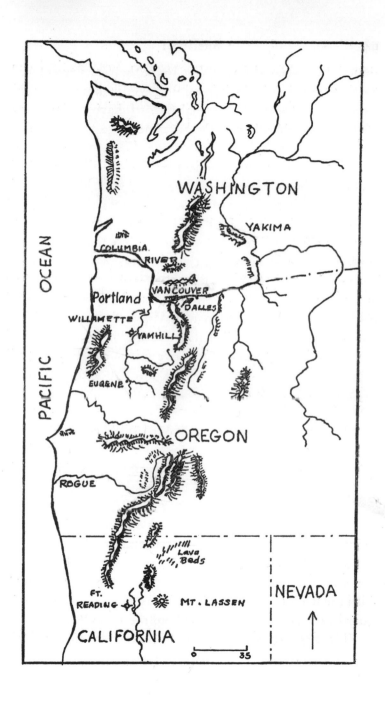

tinued. "Graduated from West Point the year you entered. At times my job looks impossible." Williamson waved his hand at the Cascade Range ahead. "I have to lay out a route for a railroad from the Sacramento to the Columbia, and I need your help."

Phil was ready, eager to do anything Williamson asked.

The engineer untied the front of his buckskin shirt and, from an inside pocket, pulled out a map. "This strip map," he said, "such as it is, is all we have to go on. We have to discover a route where the slopes are less than twelve per cent. There must be ballast close by, for a roadbed. I have to consider geology as well as the terrain. You can't just run around mountains, you have to avoid the swamps, and bridges over streams cost money. We're also experimenting with the barometer. I think it can be used in surveying. And we're making a decent map as we go. We'll have to pull together like a team of horses, Phil. You and your forty dragoons are important."

Phil drank in every word.

"At the start of each day," Mr. Williamson went on, "I'll tell you and George Crook what I'm going to do. I want protection for the surveying parties. We can't work if we are bothered. Crook is senior to you, I believe."

"Yes, sir."

"The daily plan goes like this. You and your dragoons scout far ahead and select the next campsite. By 'campsite' I mean water and a pleasant place to stop. You also furnish the advance and rear guards, and sometimes help Crook with the flank protection. His infantrymen are also the train guards, the reserve, and help about the camp."

This was the responsibility Phil wanted. It was a big

step from reconnoitering with only Private Frankman. A Cooper's hawk sailed in above them for a landing on a bare arm of a tremendous red cedar. It was wild country. The Cascades, sawtooth after sawtooth, stretched north as far as you could see.

For two months Phil was in the saddle ten hours a day. He liked the life and was sorry when the Williamson party turned into less wild but even more beautiful country near Eugene, Oregon, and down the redwood and cedar forests of the Willamette Valley to Portland.

Hardly had Phil and his dragoons pitched camp on a grassy slope near Fort Vancouver, on the banks of the mighty Columbia River, when a sergeant dashed into the fort on a horse that was about to collapse. The sergeant was a member of an Army party sent up the Columbia to punish Yakima Indians who had murdered the white agent assigned to care for them. "I regret to report the Indians beat us," the sergeant said. Then he gave the colonel a detailed description.

The colonel of the fort sent for Phil. "Mr. Sheridan," he said, "take your dragoons, march up the river, and report for duty to Major Rains. Tell him this is a disgrace. We can't have the Army whipped. Let the Indians get the upper hand, the whole country around here is lost."

Phil rode at the head of his dragoons ninety miles up the wild river, past the Cascade rapids where the torrent plunged over falls twenty-five feet high, and on to the rocky, barren country of The Dalles. Here the walls of the canyon gave Phil a feeling of being shut in. His column was strung out on the narrow trail and this did not make him happy. He knew he and his men could be easily attacked.

After two more days in the saddle, Phil reported to Major Rains. Gabriel Rains, a West Point graduate, was cautious. He wore chin whiskers that waggled when he talked. He reminded Phil of a billy-goat. "You take the head of the column, sir," Rains drawled in his North Carolina accent. "You're my advance guard. Head for the Yakima Range. Look out. Perfect ambush country."

Two days later Phil had a problem in engineering at a cold, swift stream. He got his men across without accident. Suddenly, the Yakimas attacked. Bullets zipped into the trees overhead and branches fluttered down on Phil. The valley echoed from the gunfire. He and his men threw themselves from their horses and fought on foot. Horseholders led the horses quickly to the rear, just like a drill.

Bullets cracked. There was confusion. Major Rains lost three men in the stream, bringing the main body of soldiers across. Six hundred Yakimas in war paint and feathers yelled and screamed from the sides of the canyon, and then pulled back to a ridge.

The next day the Yakimas withdrew to another ridge. Phil fastened his field glasses on them. It dawned on him that the Indians were not anxious to fight. Phil saluted the major. "Sir, let me and my men charge them. Then you follow up. We can win that way."

"Not on your tintype!" said Rains. "Six hundred Indians, and you want to charge them with forty men! Supposing you fail?"

Later the soldiers learned from a prisoner that the Indians did not wish to fight. They were shielding the escape of their women and children. The chance to attack the Indians did not come again, for cold weather and deep snow ended the campaign. Phil was disgusted with Rains. So was the colonel. So were pioneers all over the West, for this tie battle made Indians braver everywhere in Oregon.

In the next few years Phil added to his reputation of being a fearless leader, one not afraid to take a chance against odds. He fought Cascade and Yakima Indians along the Columbia. He punished the Rogue River Indians in their country. His fame spread to Washington City, where General Scott, the head of the Army, praised Phil's bravery in a written order.

At the fort at Yamhill, Oregon, Phil received a letter from his mother. It was ten days out of St. Joe, Missouri, by Pony Rider Express. His mother had written it exactly thirty days before. It seemed like magic. His mother's scrawl on thin paper told of seeing, on a trip to Chicago, *. . . a tall politician with arms like an ape, who made a speech about slavery and the Union. The man said, "A house divided against itself cannot stand." A great leader. His name is Abe Lincoln.*

Lying in his tent, Phil went over the words time and again. *A house divided against itself cannot stand.*

Later Phil learned that Abe Lincoln, "the Rail Splitter," was elected President. Phil was pleased. He read again his mother's letter and its unforgettable sentence.

One day a dispatch rider rode into the little post and pulled a battered copy of *Harper's Weekly* from his saddlebags. It had a terrible picture on its cover. It showed the United States fort in Charleston Harbor being bombarded by Confederate cannon. Phil felt helpless. He was three thousand miles from the danger.

A sergeant saluted Phil. He was covered with dust. "Sir, I'm Sergeant Adams, advance scout for Captain Archer."

"Yes?" said Phil. He knew that Captain James Archer, Ninth Infantry, was marching his company, in accordance with orders, to take over command of the fort at Yamhill.

"The thing of it is," the sergeant said, "Captain Archer is not loyal to the Union. He intends to fight for the South." The sergeant raised his right hand. "So help me," he said. "I heard you're from Ohio."

Phil questioned the sergeant at length.

I am only a second lieutenant, Phil decided, *but here is where I have a showdown with a captain.*

Phil readied his dragoons. There was an unhappy hour's wait until Captain Archer and his company marched up. Captain Archer, on horseback, swung his dusty soldiers in line in front of the fort and received Phil's salute. The captain returned it grandly, with a flash of his saber. "I'm here to take command of this post," the captain said.

Phil's heart was in his mouth. "Sir," he said, "I respect your rank, but I hear you are a Southern sympathizer. I will not give up the fort."

Archer glared down at Phil. Archer's face turned red. He placed his hand on his sword. "This is insubordination, sir," he thundered. "I will have you court-martialed and kicked out of the Army."

Phil did not change his mind, and shortly Captain Archer resigned and departed for the Confederacy.

In early 1861 the Pony Rider Express brought news that South Carolina had seceded from the Union and other states were following. Many Army officers whose homes were in the South submitted their resignations. In February, Jefferson Davis became President of the Confederacy. Phil felt heartsick, angry, and as though he might as well be in China. Problems with the Indians seemed small.

In May the riders brought word that President Lincoln had ordered the Southern ports blockaded. In July the daring Pony Riders flashed across the plains with news of a battle: "40,000 Americans killed at Bull Run."

"I don't believe it," Phil told his dragoons.

Soon word filtered west that a large part of the Yankee Army had run from the Bull Run battlefield in Virginia. The total casualties reached over four thousand.

Phil Sheridan felt like a caged lion, until one day a general order arrived promoting him to captain and ordering him to Jefferson Barracks in St. Louis. He wasted no time packing. He wanted to be in the fight.

Phil told his brave dragoons good-bye and rode to Portland. Then he sailed for San Francisco, Panama, New York City—and the terrible Civil War.

CHAPTER 11

"All I Want Is a Chance"

CINDERS clicked against the windows of the train as it approached St. Louis. The funnel-shaped stack of the engine let out a low-pitched moan as it neared a crossing. Phil touched his black moustache and smiled. When he had stopped for a quick visit in Somerset, his mother pretended she was shocked over his moustache. "Phil! The idea!" she had said. "It makes you look too old."

"That's why I raised it, Mother."

A passenger across the aisle brushed the cinders from the red plush seat and leaned toward Phil. "Captain, the last time I was in St. Looey hundreds of Confederate flags flew from the windows. Don't think you'll see many now."

"I'm glad," Phil said. "I don't want to have to fight my way from the train."

Shortly after Phil's arrival in the city General Halleck sent for him. The sign on the door read:

MAJOR GENERAL HENRY W. HALLECK
Department Commander
for
Missouri, Iowa, Minnesota, Illinois
Arkansas and Western Kentucky

While Phil waited to be admitted he wondered what his assignment would be. What kind of job would General Halleck give him? Phil knew Halleck only by reputation. Many officers did not like "Old Brains." They gave him that nickname because they said he was fussy, a time-waster, and a writer of textbooks on soldiering when he knew nothing about it. Phil felt he could get along with almost anyone—all he wanted was a chance to fight.

When Phil's name was called by an aide-de-camp, he walked smartly into the big office and saluted an owlish-looking officer behind a desk.

"Sir, Captain Philip—"

"Yes, yes, I know," the general said. "Sit down, sit down." General Halleck moved a pile of papers to the side. "I hear you're a worker, Captain Sheridan. That's why I sent for you."

Phil grinned. He did not know what to say.

General Halleck ran his hand over his bald head and picked up a paper. "I have here a contract, one of many. Left here by the Pathfinder, Frémont—you know, General Frémont. Dramatic fellow. I guess he did great work in the Rockies, but here . . ." General Halleck made a face and waved his hand over his desk. "He left us—well, you might say a mess. Probably wasn't his fault. He was surrounded by worthless staff officers. A lot of these contracts will bear scrutiny—looking into. You with me so far?"

"Yes, sir."

"Good."

"Sir, may I say something?"

"Certainly."

"Sir, I want combat."

General Halleck rubbed his elbows and laughed. "You're refreshing," he said. "Well, I can't give you a chance to fight now, but maybe later. I've got a big job right here for you. Millions of dollars are involved. I hear you have integrity and can be trusted."

Phil sat up straighter. "Thank you," he said. He liked General Halleck.

For two months Phil studied contracts and checked the accounts left by General Frémont. Just after Christmas General Halleck sent for Phil again.

"You've done fine work," the old general said. "I'm giving you a new job."

"In combat, sir?"

"Nope." The general chuckled. He admired the small, broad-shouldered captain. Halleck said, "You remind me of a tough bantam." He laughed again. "I'm going to make you chief commissary officer and chief quartermaster for Curtis' army. He has eleven thousand men. You must see they are supplied with food, ammunition, and clothing. And check their wagon trains. This is necessary if we are to win."

Phil was delighted. This was not combat, but at least he would be in the field with an army.

"This army's going to fight soon," Halleck said. "That's a secret you need to know."

Phil plunged into his work. He angered some of the colonels by taking mules and horses from their regiments, if they had too many, and giving the animals to regiments that needed them. "But this is our private regimental property," the colonels howled.

"General Halleck said we have to win," Phil countered. "We can't win unless each regiment has a supply train. Each regiment has to have food, extra shoes, and ammunition."

Major General Curtis was the commander of the army moving into southwest Missouri and Arkansas, and he was a hard man to work for. Phil spent long hours in the saddle. He was happy but he felt he belonged in combat. For General Curtis, Phil saw that supplies went forward as soon as wagons were loaded, that the teamsters drove carefully over the forlorn dirt roads, and that empty wagons were driven back promptly for more supplies. When there was a railroad strike, General Halleck sent Phil ten thousand dollars and told him to settle it. Phil solved the labor problem and the strikers went back to work.

Phil began to believe that he would spend the war as commissary officer and quartermaster, until an incident happened which made him wonder what he was in for. Some officers stole some horses from civilians who were Confederates. The officers asked Phil to buy the animals for the Army.

Phil refused. "I never buy stolen property," he said.

The thieves went to see General Curtis. They painted Phil as a man who bought only from favorites.

Curtis sent for Phil. Phil told the truth, but the handsome general chose to believe the men who saw him first. Phil was in trouble.

Phil's temper rose when the general reprimanded him. Phil said bluntly, "I will not buy stolen horses and no one can make me do it. *No* one—not even you."

General Curtis shook with anger. The gold-fringed epaulets on his blue uniform quivered. He pointed at Phil. "You are no longer my commissary officer. You are through. Get out! You will hear from me shortly, young man. Stand by for a court-martial."

Phil was crushed and angry. He took the train back to St. Louis to see his friend, General Halleck. Phil explained matters to the old general and finished, "Sir, General Curtis is going to put me before a court-martial. Sir, I wish you would give me a chance to fight."

Halleck's bald head wrinkled. "Not now," he said, "not now. Don't worry about yourself or Curtis. I know you're honest and I have a job for you. You know about horses, I'm sure."

Before Phil could reply, Halleck said, "We use up horses faster than a shoemaker uses nails. I want you to go up to Madison and Racine, Wisconsin, and buy horses for my department. See the adjutant for details and the paymaster for money."

Phil felt better but he wished the old general would give him a chance to lead soldiers in battle. Phil's West Point classmates were distinguishing themselves. Many were majors. Jim Birdseye McPherson was a colonel. Hank Slocum, badly wounded at Bull Run, had recovered and was a brigadier general. Dave Stanley also wore the one star of a brigadier. Buying horses seemed to be a one-way street leading to nowhere. Phil felt his classmates were passing him by.

When Phil was examining horses, he heard news of the battle at Shiloh. He placed the two hundred horses he had purchased on a freight train and hurried to St. Louis. "I'll take a chance," he muttered. "I'll ask the old general once more to please let me fight."

But General Halleck had gone south to Shiloh, and at his desk sat Colonel John Kelton. The colonel listened. When Phil finished, he said, "I can't give you a fighting command, Sheridan, but there's a hospital ship going up the Tennessee this afternoon to bring back another load of wounded from Shiloh. I give you permission to go down there and see General Halleck. Ask him for yourself."

Phil wrung the colonel's hand and streaked for the steamboat landing. On board he listened to accounts of the battle. It was one of the hardest fought of all time. Phil was sorry he had missed it.

The battle had been over for two weeks when Phil arrived at Pittsburg Landing, near the Shiloh battlefield. Four steamers were anchored to the bank, smoke from their twin stacks floating almost to heaven. One steamboat was about to cast off for Cincinnati with a load of wounded. You could hear the groans of the mangled men.

Near a little house on the bank stood General Halleck. He was surrounded by staff officers. Phil sat down on a log nearby and waited. He clasped his hands nervously. He felt as if his future depended on what Halleck would say. Every now and then Phil picked up a sentence of General Halleck's: "Our three armies won't move a foot until we are completely reorganized. . . . We'll move south behind entrenchments. . . . Our advance will be slow but safe. . . ."

Halleck caught sight of Phil and recognized him with a

flick of the hand. Phil's spirits zoomed. Halleck seemed friendly.

When the conference was over the old general walked to Phil. Phil sprang to attention, saluted, and smiled.

"Well, Captain Sheridan, did you bring those horses down here?" The general rubbed his elbows and grinned. "I know—you want a chance to fight."

"Yes, sir."

"Don't know of any command that needs a leader right now, but you can help about the camp. See Colonel Thom and tell him I want you to work. I'll see you later, young man."

At least he didn't send me back, Phil thought.

General Halleck was delighted with the improvements Phil made about his camp. Phil procured fresh beef and cooks who could cook it. And when Phil was about to become bored with camp life, lightning struck. Governor Blair of Michigan offered Phil command of the 2nd Michigan Cavalry, and Halleck talked to Phil about it.

"All I want is a chance," Phil said. He could hardly wait for the answer.

"I'm giving it to you," Halleck said, "and I'm promoting you to colonel. Here's a pair of silver eagles. I hope they bring you good luck. You'd better leave at once. The Second Michigan is moving out right now to go on a raid."

Phil shook the general's hand. He felt as though he were graduating from school. He sprinted to the cooks' tents and placed coffee, sugar, bacon, and hardtack in his saddlebags.

When he was galloping through the forest to catch his regiment, Phil thought back to Fort Reading. At least he

had more food in his saddlebags than he did when he left
Reading to catch Mr. Williamson.

Phil rode up to the brigadier general commanding the
raid and reported. The Michigan general looked Phil over
carefully. The general saw that Phil sat his horse with ease.

"We're riding deep into enemy territory," the general
said. "We're going to cut around on a circle behind the
enemy lines. Our job is to tear up the railroad—that's the
Mobile and Ohio—so the Rebels can't use it in case they
come north. Go ahead and take command of your regiment."

Phil hesitated. "Sir, can you tell me anything about this
regiment?"

"You have eight hundred and twenty-seven good Wolverines. The best officer, I think, is Captain Alger. He's
sick with a fever, but he's up there sittin' on his horse."

Phil's uncertainty, caused by riding into Confederate
territory with men he did not know, soon vanished. The
Michigan Wolverines were anxious to fight, and Phil liked
them. In the two days' ride through woods and farmlands
he met as many of the officers and soldiers as he could. At
the end of the second day the force separated and Phil's
regiment rode on alone.

At Booneville, Mississippi, they struck the railroad, and
Phil dismounted his horsemen. Prying rails from ties was
hard and slow. Someone discovered that the best thing to
do was to rip up whole sections of track and place everything on the fire.

Phil sent scouts in all directions. He did not want to be
surprised. He trotted over some of the trails himself.

When he rode back to the railroad, long stretches of track

were wrecked. Twenty-six cars, ten thousand rifles, and three cannons were on the fires. His men presented him with a leather dispatch case they had found in a car. Inside the case were Confederate plans. Phil was happy. He was sure his work would stop Confederates from using the railroad for months, and that the captured plans were valuable.

The Wolverines were cocky. No one seemed to worry about the telltale column of black smoke pouring upward.

Suddenly a corporal galloped across a field from the outpost line deep in the woods. "Colonel Sheridan," he half-shouted, "Confederate troops headin' this way. Lots of 'em." The breeze bore out the corporal's words. *Crack, crack, crack* came the echoes.

A major said to Phil, "We had better get out of here while we have the chance, sir."

"Chance?" snapped Phil. "That's what I want, a chance to fight."

A lieutenant drew his sword and grinned. "Colonel, you make me want to take a chance with you."

Phil stopped the work of destruction. His men picked up their heavy rifles. They checked their loads.

Phil left one hundred men behind as a reserve, in case trouble sprang from another direction, and to take care of the horses. He formed his seven hundred men in line and ordered them toward the enemy.

At the edge of the wood a Wolverine lieutenant brought a Confederate soldier to Phil. The man was badly frightened. "Yes, sir," the prisoner said, "I'll answer your questions. I'm a God-fearin' man. I have had enough."

"Who is the Confederate commander," said Phil, "and how many men has he?"

"Gen'l Chalmers, sir, and he's five thousand infantry-men. I guarantee."

"How do you know?" said Phil. "If you are telling the truth I may let you go home. If you are lying—"

The man looked earnestly in Phil's face. "I wouldn't lie at a time like this, sir. I've seen our regiment on parade time and again. There's our regiment and six others. Yes-tiddy our cap'n said that the quartermaster had a hard time feedin' five thousand men." The prisoner trembled.

Phil thought the matter over. *How long could eight hundred and twenty-seven Wolverines hold five thousand?*

A Wolverine captain ran up. "Colonel Sheridan, they are reinforcing their skirmish line." At the same time the crash of the battle became louder. A bullet whined over Phil's head.

A train whistled to the rear. Phil said to the officer, "Take my horse and gallop back. Get a couple of men from the reserve. Capture that engineer and make him keep blowing his whistle."

Phil walked through the woods. Confederate infantry stood firing, a hundred yards away. Clouds of bitter-tasting black powder filled the woods. Suddenly the train began to toot its whistle.

Phil grinned. "Maybe they'll think we have reinforce-ments," he told his men.

Phil's poise was contagious. His dismounted cavalrymen worked their new Henry repeating rifles faster. The Union soldiers could fire more shots per minute with the Henry than could the Confederates, who were equipped with al-most every kind of weapon. A corporal near Phil was shot in the leg and fell to the ground screaming.

Phil turned to the orderly who was following him. "Where is Captain Alger?"

"Back near the railroad, sick. His fellows put up a tent for him."

Phil galloped to the captain's tent and threw himself from his horse. Captain Alger stood up. His face was flushed. Phil placed his hand on the captain's forehead. "You don't have much fever," Phil said. "Do you want to get in on this? I hear you're a leader. I can use you."

"Yes, sir."

"I'm going to take a chance and surprise them," Phil said. "I want you to take ninety men out of the reserve, ride around to the right, and strike them from the rear." Phil pointed out a trail over which he had ridden earlier in the day.

Shortly, Captain Alger and ninety horsemen were trotting away.

Phil and his men were outnumbered six to one. He was taking his reserve, and he was splitting his command in the face of the enemy. He swallowed. He hoped everything would work all right.

An hour dragged. Phil hauled out his watch countless times. Captain Alger had one hour to get behind the enemy. When an hour had elapsed, Phil would order his own line forward. A captain ran back from the firing line. "We had better be getting out," he said to Phil. "We can't hold any longer."

But Phil waited. He felt anxious. Fifteen minutes to go and no sign of Alger.

On the hour, Phil's men attacked. In a few minutes Captain Alger charged the Confederates from the rear, his men yelling, his bugler sounding the charge. The Confederates thought they were outnumbered.

Phil waved his sword in one hand. With his other he fired his pistol and charged into the smoke with his men. He screamed and cursed.

The Confederates broke and ran.

Captain Alger's riders dashed through the Confederates. Alger's horse galloped under a low branch, and the captain fell at Phil's feet. The captain rose to his knees.

"Are you all right?" Phil asked.

"Yes, sir. I don't have my pistol."

Phil gave Alger his pistol and picked up another from a dead Confederate. Phil held it up, hat and sword in the other hand. He shouted at the top of his lungs, "Oh, God, who art the author of peace and lover of concord! Go on! Get that last bunch!"

His men looked at him in amazement. A sergeant said later, "It jest didn't seem right, him leading us in a fight yellin' bloody murder, then spoutin' the Bible."

Phil's soldiers wondered what he would do next. The battlefield was dotted with wounded—many of them screaming. Over on the tracks the engine had run out of steam and had stopped blowing its whistle.

A messenger saluted Phil. He handed Phil a written order from the Michigan brigadier general. *Colonel Sheridan,* the message read, *your position is too exposed. We cannot support you if you run into superior numbers. Pull your men back nine miles at once to our camp at Rienzi, Mississippi.*

Phil looked up the doctor and gave him help to load the wounded onto wagons. He and his horsemen were in high spirits as they walked their horses back north on the dirt road. They had ridden into Confederate country, destroyed railroad track and weapons the Confederacy needed, had defeated five thousand men, and had prisoners to prove it, and had lost but few men.

When Phil rode back down the column to check the rear guard, the Wolverines cheered. "Hooray for Little Phil!" they shouted. Cold chills ran up and down his spine. It was the first time in his career he had been cheered by soldiers, but it would not be the last.

Word of Phil's daring in the face of a large force went around the Union camps. Five brigadier generals signed a telegram to General Halleck, who had been ordered to Washington as advisor to President Lincoln and to be general-in-chief. The wire said: GOOD BRIGADIERS ARE SCARCE. WE BEG YOU TO PROMOTE COLONEL PHIL SHERIDAN. HE IS WORTH HIS WEIGHT IN GOLD. HE BROUGHT US CAPTURED LETTERS OF IMMENSE VALUE AND THE REBEL PLANS.

In the capital, General Halleck was busy readying the Union Army after its defeat by General Robert E. Lee and Stonewall Jackson at the Second Battle of Bull Run. But Halleck was not too busy to write at once to the Secretary of War and tell him about his young friend, Colonel Phil Sheridan. The Secretary of War took the writing to President Lincoln.

The way Sheridan courted danger and won encouraged Union hopes at a gloomy time. Phil Sheridan was the talk of the North, but greater danger lay ahead for him.

CHAPTER 12

The Battle of Perryville

TORCHES of pitch and "light wood" illuminated the railroad. Two engines snorted, ready to pull their trains north. Phil inspected each boxcar to make sure the horses were not too crowded. Here and there an animal refused to go up the ramp leading into a boxcar and the Wolverines had to push.

Captain Campbell, of headquarters, led a jet black horse up to Phil. Phil knew the horse, Rienzi. The captain jumped aside to keep the big animal from stepping on his feet. The horse raised his head, switched his tail, and pranced.

"Colonel," the captain said, "I'm making you a present of Rienzi. I don't fancy riding. Oh, I wouldn't transfer from the cavalry for the world, but I'm getting me a tamer horse. Rienzi, he is for you. He's yours."

Phil shook the captain's hand and stroked the animal's nose. The withers of the horse were as high as Phil's head. Phil sprang on the animal's bare back and trotted along the train of boxcars, and on to the train of wooden coaches. The

Wolverines cheered when they saw their leader. When he rode back, Phil tried to pay Campbell for the horse. "No, sir," the captain said. "He's a present from me to you."

Phil was delighted. Rienzi was the most powerful horse he had ever ridden.

Phil gathered his Wolverines around. Their faces looked gaunt in the torchlight. Above the puffing of the engines, Phil shouted, "I am telling you all I know. Two Confederate armies under Braxton Bragg and Kirby Smith are heading north up through Tennessee and Kentucky. We are taking the Mobile and Ohio to Columbus, Kentucky, and from there on we'll ride steamboats. We have been ordered to help stop the invasion."

"We'll stop them!" a Wolverine shouted.

Phil shook his fist at an imaginary enemy in the sky. His Wolverines howled.

At Columbus, on the Mississippi River, the regiment and its horses climbed aboard five gunboats. Phil was on the texas deck of the lead steamer. It was pleasant watching the bank slip by. The captain bowed to him and said, "Colonel, you know the sides of this gunboat are tin. There are Confederate batteries two miles up the river. I hate to chance it in daylight. Suppose we steam up a ways, then lay to and make a run for it at night?"

"Pull over and tie up," Phil said. "Signal the other gunboats. My orders say to help run the Rebels south. We might as well start now." To his orderly, Phil said, "When Rienzi is unloaded, bring him up front to me."

In four hours Phil's expedition was back at the gunboats. He was disgusted. He snapped impatiently at the captain, "Get up steam. No Rebels around. All we found were people up in Caseyville waving the Stars and Stripes."

When the Wolverines landed at Louisville, Kentucky, Phil galloped Rienzi to the headquarters of General "Bull" Nelson to pay his respects. The three-hundred-pound general was in bed, sick. He said, "Sheridan, what in hell are you doing wearing colonel's eagles? Didn't you see the orders from Washington making you a brigadier general?"

"I can't believe it," Phil said. His black eyes sparkled. He felt six feet tall.

"Well, I guarantee it," said the giant. "Here, reach in my carpetbag. It's in that wardrobe closet. You'll find a beat-up pair of general's stars. They are yours. Congratulations."

Phil walked out of the headquarters feeling that nothing could stop him now. This was unusual recognition. He wrote home.

Then, when things were brightest, he received orders to give up his Wolverines and to take command of the 11th Infantry Division. He felt sick, for he loved the Michigan cavalrymen. He inspected his new division, six thousand two hundred infantrymen from Illinois, Missouri, Ohio, Michigan, and Wisconsin.

For two weeks Phil drilled his soldiers and his two batteries of artillery. Suddenly, orders came for him to report to General Buell. Phil knew that Buell was the man the Union depended upon to stop the invasion.

At Buell's headquarters there was confusion. Aides-de-camp and orderlies held horses outside the building because there were not enough hitching racks. Inside, staff officers scurried about with papers.

Phil gave his name to an adjutant. "Yes, sir, General

Sheridan," the adjutant said. "General Buell said to send you in at once. Just a minute."

Phil felt nervous. He knew that Buell, a Mexican War veteran, was not popular with all of his officers. There were many stories about General Don Buell. He loved, they said, to show off his physical strength; sometimes he would hold up his wife with one hand and place her on the mantel. Phil wished he could see that. Buell seemed a sort of Halleck, more of a teacher than a fighting, daring leader.

"Come this way, sir," the adjutant said. "The general is anxious to see you."

Buell, almost as small as Phil, wore a pointed beard and white side whiskers, which framed his face. He had eyes that saw through you. The general walked around from behind his desk and shook Phil's hand. "Glad to have you in my army," Buell said. "We need fighters. A big fight coming up. How is the Eleventh Division?"

"Fine, sir. A bit green, but they'll do."

General Buell nodded his satisfaction. He stepped to a wall map and raised its curtain. "This is what we face. Two Confederate armies—sixty thousand men—that's what they have. And what do I have? I have sixty thousand, too, if you count the sick, cooks, hangers on, teamsters, and sutlers. A dog-eat-dog battle is ahead. Does the Eleventh have its Colors?"

"Yes, sir."

"Good. About half of my army doesn't even have them. Men fight better when they can see their flag."

Phil thought back to the Cadet Chapel at West Point. He could hear old General Scott's voice once again, "Units led by love of country are the best."

"I'm counting on you, Sheridan," Buell said. "There'll be an officers' call shortly. I want you to listen in." Buell tinkled a little bell on his desk and an aide-de-camp answered.

"Bring 'em all in," Buell said.

Phil was the youngest general in the room by ten years. He was happy to see General George Thomas again. Thomas, a big burly fellow, had taught Phil cavalry and artillery tactics at West Point. Thomas was second in command of Buell's army. Phil knew of Thomas' staunch reputation. When he was a cadet he had threatened to throw an upperclassman out of a window for hazing a friend.

Near Buell and the National Colors stood a blond lieutenant, one arm in a sling.

"This is Mr. Aldine," Buell said. "Loyal lieutenant from Florida. He refused to surrender when four thousand, one hundred and thirty-three soldiers wearing our uniform laid down their arms at Munfordville, Kentucky. Aldine may lose the use of his arm, but at least he has his honor. I won't talk any more. Go ahead, sir."

Hanna Aldine jutted out his jaw. "I was in charge of the scouts for Colonel Wilder at Munfordville. It was my job to scout the country out. Two days before the surrender I rode into the fort to tell Colonel Wilder that a large bunch of Rebs were coming—that if they arrived they might surround us. The colonel, Colonel Wilder—"

Buell interrupted. "Wilder had four thousand, one hundred and thirty-three Union soldiers," he boiled. Then he nodded at the scout and said, "Excuse me."

"Yes, sir," said the scout. "After they surrounded the

fort the Confederates sent an officer in under a white flag and said that Colonel Wilder should surrender, that if he didn't a lot of our men would be killed. Colonel Wilder was worried. He said he didn't know the ropes. He sent the white flag back and called us officers in. Colonel Wilder said that when trouble came, back in his factory in Indiana, he knew what to do, but that military goings-on were strange. He put surrendering to a vote. The officers were divided fifty-fifty, about half for fighting their way out and about half for surrendering. Colonel Wilder told us he knew General Buckner on the Confederate side was a gentleman. He said that he would go over under a white flag and ask General Buckner what to do."

Buell hit his desk a blow. "Can you beat that?" he shouted. "Wilder went to an enemy general and asked him what to do!"

"General Buckner refused to tell him," continued the blond lieutenant. "He *did* let Colonel Wilder count their cannon. Colonel Wilder came back and said it was a kind of hair-splitting job as far as he could see, that we were to lay down our weapons and march out of the fort with our hands up. Major Trimble said he was for at least setting fire to the stores, but Colonel Wilder said he didn't think it was right when you surrendered. We marched out. Several of us who didn't fancy a prison camp made a break for it. I was one of the lucky ones."

"Thank you," General Buell said. He shook the scout's hand. Tears of anger filled Buell's eyes. Phil felt as though he himself were responsible for the disgrace.

"Twenty-two years ago," Buell said, "I had it drummed into me when I was a cadet that the best defense is determined defenders." Buell lost control of his temper. His face became purple. He shouted, "I want that to permeate this army! You see to it!" He calmed himself. He straightened his uniform and shook the scout's hand again. "I am promoting you to captain as of now," Buell said, glaring at the generals. "That's all. We can't win by surrendering."

The march toward the Confederates was trying. Phil's aggressive spirit chafed. Buell was cautious. His army crawled along at a snail's pace. He thought he was up against a superior force and he did not want to be trapped. Rienzi wore Phil out. The horse walked faster than the infantrymen, and Phil tugged and tugged on the reins to hold the animal down.

It was July weather in October. The sun was merciless. The uniforms of the Eleventh became powder blue, then dusty white. Men sneezed and coughed. It was hard for Phil and his officers to keep the men closed up. They strayed to the woods alongside the road—anywhere to avoid the choking, oppressive dust.

When Phil rode up and down the column there was no cheering. The men chanted, "Water! Water! Water!"

Phil rode back to one of Buell's generals. "The men must have water," Phil said. "They can't go much farther without it."

The general searched his map. He poked it toward Phil. "Can you go ahead and capture Doctor's Creek?"

"I never captured a creek," Phil said, "but here goes!"

The Confederates on the creek's bank peppered Phil's skirmishers. Phil galloped Rienzi up behind the leading wave. He studied the enemy with his field glasses, between gaps in the clouds of black powder. The enemy fire was erratic. It did not sound as loud as the battle against General Chalmers' men in Mississippi. Phil ordered a battery of his field artillery to the flank. Phil galloped to the spot where he wanted the guns.

The sturdy horses pulling the cannons and ammunition dashed up. The cannoneers leaped from the caissons and manhandled the guns, pointing them toward the Confederates.

"Canister!" Phil shouted to the battery commander.

The cannoneers loaded the guns with canister—shells filled with small bits of rusty scrap iron, lead balls, slugs, and iron pellets. The four cannons roared. The terrible canister whizzed through the woods. Men screamed and fell. Gray-clad cavalry under the daring "Fightin' Joe" Wheeler galloped up. As if in punishment for the canister, they charged Phil's flank. But his line held and Buell's army had water.

Just before dark Phil led his men up on a ridge and ordered them to dig small, shallow holes into which they might curl and shoot if the enemy struck. He placed his two batteries where they could protect the ends of his line.

That night Phil rode Rienzi to a conference. It was in a large tent a mile to the rear. An officer said, "General Sheridan, when you were at West Point didn't you have some trouble with a cadet named Terrill?"

"Yes," said Phil flatly. He felt the hair on the back of his head stand up. Even though it was a long time ago he felt a surge of anger. *Terrill cost me a year at West Point,* he said to himself.

"He commands a brigade of the Tenth Ohio not far from here," the officer said. "He's a brigadier general."

After the conference Phil rode the big horse back toward his division. His thoughts were on Terrill. Phil felt ashamed that he still thought of him as an enemy. "We are both fighting for the Union," Phil muttered.

He turned Rienzi around and searched for the Tenth Ohio. He found Terrill. Phil could hardly believe that the man in front of him had once been the harsh, snippy cadet sergeant. Terrill had grown taller. His wide moustache and goatee made him look years older, more dignified, but there was still the same sharp nose and broad forehead. "I'm Sheridan," Phil said, extending his hand. "Came down to say hello."

They sat beside a campfire together for a half-hour and talked of their experiences in the peacetime army. When Phil finally called for his horse, Terrill said, "Phil, it means a lot to me that you came to bury the hatchet. I was wrong —dead wrong."

"You can't bear all the blame," Phil said. "I learned a lesson. My temper—I can control it now. Good luck, Bill. I'll see you after the battle." The two former enemies shook hands and parted friends.

When Buell's men in blue got up the next morning they built hundreds of little fires. They huddled about them, three or four men to a fire. The ridge which Phil's men held was soon wreathed in light-blue smoke. His men cooked bacon and tried to mop up its grease with hardtack. They washed their breakfast down with coffee. Suddenly the Rebel Yell broke over the landscape. It was a long-drawn-out screech sounding like the hinges of Hell.

Long lines of Confederates came marching toward the Union positions. Confederate drummer boys tapped their drums so the soldiers could keep step. The gray lines guided on their Stars and Bars. Confederate artillery banged cannon balls into Union positions. You could see the red battle flags of the Confederates through the smoke and flying dirt. The Rebels marched straight for the Yankees. The Yankee artillery opened up. The noise was deafening.

Phil rode Rienzi everywhere. The black horse, terrified by the noise and crash of the guns, ran like the wind. Phil was excited. He yelled, "Aim low! Steady!" His Eleventh Division, crouching in its rifle pits, pouring bullets into the Confederate lines, did not give. Green troops under Terrill streaked for the rear.

A mounted messenger from general headquarters raced his horse along the ridge and caught Phil. "Sir, a dispatch for you."

Phil read the scrawl twice. He could not understand. It said, *General Sheridan—Do not bring on an engagement.* Phil threw the paper away and cursed.

He galloped toward a battery commander. He waved his sword and screamed, "Fire faster! You can fire faster than that!" Phil rode away. In five minutes he was back. "Captain, when I give the word, our line is going forward. Six regiments of our division will counterattack. Be ready to get your horses up here, limber up quickly, and move forward. Take position on that knoll about a half-mile ahead." Phil pointed with his sword. "You go into battery fast. You hear me?"

Phil's part of Buell's line was the only part to counterattack.

Phil's men drove the enemy back and on through the village of Perryville. While the fighting was going on the town was like a ghost town. But when Phil's rear guard marched through, a host of Negroes brought the soldiers water and fruit.

When the battle stopped at four in the afternoon, a staff officer from Buell's headquarters rode up. He congratulated Phil on the performance of the Eleventh. Phil was still excited. He brushed the praise aside. "How did the battle come out?" he demanded.

"I guess it was a tie," the staff officer said. "Only nine of our fifteen brigades got in the fighting. There was an acoustic shadow that hurt us."

"What the hell is that?" Phil said.

"An acoustic shadow is caused by peculiar air and terrain conditions. A strange wind kept the noise of the battle from being heard in General Buell's headquarters, and we were only two and a half miles away. We didn't even know there was a fight."

Phil swore under his breath. He made a mental note to insure that no "acoustic shadow" ever tricked him.

"Heavy losses," said the staff officer. "We lost well over four thousand. I think that's more than the Confederates lost. General Terrill was killed."

"Terrill?" Phil could hardly believe his ears. "Why, just last night—"

"I know. He was killed trying to rally his men. Badly frightened bunch."

Phil offered a silent prayer for Terrill's soul. He was thankful that he had gone to see the Virginian.

"Yes, a tie battle, General Sheridan. The Confederates are heading for East Tennessee. We even have to take care of their dead and wounded."

"Do we have any troops after them?"

"Don't think so, General."

Phil banged his sword angrily into its scabbard. He wondered why General Buell did not follow the Confederates. *I'll never give up after a fight,* he vowed. "Acoustic shadow!" he said aloud.

Phil inspected his outpost, then walked Rienzi back over the battlefield. The wounded were still being removed by stretcher bearers. The moans of the wounded shook him. A grave-digging party was making a huge hole. The click of the shovels and the sight of the dead, Union and Confederate lying side by side awaiting burial, saddened him. The Union Army suffered a terrible toll for a tie battle.

Things looked black for the Union. On Antietam Creek in Maryland, one hundred and twenty-five thousand Union and Confederate soldiers had come to grips. The Battle of Antietam was even bloodier than Shiloh. General McClellan, of the Union Army, had not used all of his men and the Union troops were not employed as a unit. There had been no real winner.

A few days after the battle of Perryville orders from Washington City placed General Rosecrans in command of the army instead of Buell. Phil felt both sad and happy. He was sad because he liked General Don Buell, but happy because Rosecrans was one of the brigadiers who signed the telegram recommending that Phil be made a general.

Phil talked to his officers and men. "I am proud of you and what you did," he told them. "We did our share, but next time we will do even more. We want no more tie battles."

CHAPTER 13

The Battle of Stones River

ROSECRANS' army made the march to Bowling Green, Kentucky, in easy stages. On the hundred-mile hike Phil made the soldiers throw away unnecessary articles from their packs. He cut down on the officers' baggage in the wagon trains, and he made his men see why all this was necessary.

As soon as camp was pitched at Bowling Green, Phil sent scouts to scour the country.

Although his men had come through the battle at Perryville in a most creditable manner, most of them were green. He remembered how he had suppressed the "mutiny" at Bedloe's Island, and how he made soldiers out of the rebellious recruits. He worked long hours to insure that his soldiers had the best food obtainable, clean kitchens, and serviceable uniforms and shoes. When his day's work was done, Phil rode Rienzi out of camp to learn about the country.

One December evening when he returned to camp, just after Phil turned Rienzi over to a soldier so the animal could be tied to the picket line for the night, Phil's Negro servant, Zeb Marion, met Phil in front of his conical tent. "Strange gen'man to see you, Gen'ral," Zeb said.

"Who is he?"

Zeb's shoulders went up and down. "Don't know, but he's quality. A preachin' man. He's waiting for you in de aide's tent. Shall I fetch him, sah?"

Phil sat beside the Sibley stove. The glare from the red-hot stove and the candlelight made the features of the man seated nearby more rugged than they actually were. The more Phil listened to Jim Card's soft voice and almost apologetic manner, the more Phil liked him.

"In reply to yo' question, Gen'l, I'm in the Lord's business. I travel all about this country with tracts and Bibles, preachin' once in a while here and there where there's no reg'lar minister. Our country is in a sad time. I tell you, I believe its salvation lies in Abraham Lincoln and the Union Army."

"A-men," Phil said. He opened the door of the stove to cool the tent.

"I know the people of this land," Jim Card went on. "I know every road. Goodness knows I ought to. I've traveled over 'em, totin' my tracts and Bibles up and down 'em on my back for a dozen years, ever since I got the Call. That was in fifty-one."

Jim Card's honest voice and his sincere manner intrigued his listener. Card went on, "Do a little doctorin', on occasion, when a real doctor isn't around. Delivered a man-child only yestiddy at Gold City—a spankin' good one. Mother and child doing well, thank you. Before I got the Call, I tried phrenology, but I finally got it in my butt-head that my chosen work was colporter—totin' tracts and Bibles and placing them where they can spread the Word to the poor in heart."

Phil remembered he had not gone to Mass for a month. He also made a mental note to hold a conference with the chaplains to inquire about the religious welfare of the division.

"... So I come, Gen'l, to offer you my services, sir."

"But I have a full staff of chaplains. Thank you."

"No, no, no." Jim held up his hand. "I don't mean that, no sir. My three brothers and I know this country as far south as Chattanooga. We could bring you information about Mr. Reb."

Phil's mouth dropped open. He squinted at Jim Card. Phil picked up a stick and stoked the Sibley stove. He needed time to think. Card gathered a handful of sticks from the woodpile in the corner. He was just a bit taller than Phil. *He can't be a Confederate spy,* Phil thought. *If he is, he's the greatest actor since John Edmund Owens.*

"Gen'l Sheridan, my three brothers, Esau—he's the youngest, the one blessed with the Biblical name. The rest of us weren't so fortunate. There's Edward and Henry, too. We'll go forth and find how many men the enemy has, where he is, and what tricks he's up to. And we'll tell you about the roads and trails in case you wish to go there. We know who the good, loyal people are, and we can organize 'em into a system-net. All we want is the chance, Gen'l."

Phil pulled out the little meerschaum pipe he had had

from his Somerset, Ohio, days and filled it with tobacco. He wanted to think. "Tobacco?" he said to Jim Card.

"No, thank you, sir. You don't find tobacco in the Bible."

Phil chuckled. He blew a smoke ring. "Have you any identification, any proof you can give me?"

"I have the greatest proof in the world," Card said. He tugged from his pocket a small Bible.

Phil fingered the Book. It was worn and frayed. He doubted if there were any use in having Card take a loyalty oath. "Spying is dangerous work, Reverend Card. I am authorized to pay—"

Card raised his hand as if he were about to give a benediction. "Just plain 'Jim Card,' and thank you. No pay. All we Card boys want is to serve our country and to see the forces of the Lord triumphant."

Phil accepted Jim Card's services, and in fifteen days the spy was back to report. Phil was delighted to see him.

"Gen'l, the Lord has smiled on his servants, Jim and Esau. May I trouble you for a piece of paper, sir?"

The spy pulled a stub of a pencil and his Bible from his pocket. He totaled up the page numbers marked in his Book. "All I have to do now, sir, is add on two ciphers. There. They have thirty-three thousand men at arms, and if you have a map I can tell you more."

Phil called for his two most trusted colonels, G. W. Roberts and Frederick Schaefer. "Get your horses and one for Mr. Jim Card," Phil said, "and ask the aide to have Rienzi brought up at once. We're all going to see General Rosecrans."

"And who is he?" Jim Card asked.

"He's the commanding general," Phil said. "He's the leader of the Army of the Cumberland—this army."

Shortly, the four horsemen and two orderlies were cantering down the muddy road to Rosecrans' headquarters. Rosecrans, who graduated from West Point eleven years before Phil, was as straight as an arrow. Phil had seen him fly off the handle and a few moments later apologize for his temper, then give the man he had castigated a present. Rosecrans was a hard man to predict.

At headquarters Phil's party gave their horses to orderlies, and Phil announced he wanted to see General Rosecrans.

"Sorry, he's in conference with a herd of newspapermen," the adjutant general said. "I've no idea how long it will last. They are passing the bottle around in there now."

Phil gritted his teeth. He hated reporters because they often printed information that helped the Confederates.

When the newsmen finally walked out of Rosecrans' office, three civilians in swallow-tailed coats, carrying plug hats, walked by Phil and went into the general's office. Phil scrunched in his seat.

"Can't help it, General Sheridan," the adjutant general said. "General Rosecrans knows you're here, but he said to send the politicians in first."

Phil got up and paced nervously. He tried to figure out how he would run an army if he had one. It was exasperating to be shelved when one had important information.

In twenty-five minutes the door opened and Rosecrans

ushered out the civilians and beckoned to Phil and the three men with him.

"Sorry as all get-out," Rosecrans said, "but sometimes army business has to wait. You look fit, Sheridan. I wish I could get out of this office more." Rosecrans nodded to the two colonels with Phil. The general's blond beard and bushy, taffy-colored hair needed cutting. It gave him a slightly wild look. His hawklike nose crinkled a bit as he took in the mud-covered boots of the spy.

Phil introduced Jim Card and told the general of Jim's work and his background.

"I'm a religious man, too," Rosecrans said to Card. "Catholic. I curse, but I draw the line at taking the Lord's name in vain, like Sheridan does. I wish I had time to discuss the Sermon on the Mount with you, Mr. Card. Nothing I like better, but time—" Rosecrans shrugged his heavy shoulders. "Time flies around here." Then he jerked a thumb at the whiskey bottles on a nearby table. "Drink, anyone? I'm having one more."

"I only take wine," Card said, "and that in temperance."

"I don't have any of that," Rosecrans said. "Sorry. You, Sheridan?"

"Not now," Phil said.

The two colonels poured themselves a sip. Colonel Roberts, as tall and as straight as Rosecrans but not as broad, said, "Very excellent bourbon, General."

"Ought to be," said Rosecrans. "I pay six dollars and a quarter a case for it."

In a moment, Phil had Jim Card show his figures giving the strength of Bragg's Confederate army.

Rosecrans broke into a smile. He clapped the little spy on the back. "Wonderful when things jibe like this. I congratulate you. This compares within two thousand to the information I have from my scouts and from other sources. Now, Jim Card, can you tell me exactly where these Confederates are?"

Phil felt a warm glow toward Jim. From that moment, the daring spy became one of his favorite people. Phil loved anyone who would take a chance.

" 'Deed I can, Gen'l Rosycrans. Been right in their lines with my tracts. Had to, to get the numbers of their formations. That's why I checked the page numbers in the Old Book. The Rebels are hoverin' about Murfreesboro, Tennessee, one hunert and five good country miles from here. Sir, if you've a map—"

"Yes, sir," said Rosecrans. "Yes, sir."

"All right to mark on it?" Jim asked.

"Go right ahead. Please do."

"This is how they're spread out on the ground," Jim said. "Cannons sprinkled all along the line."

"This is terrific," Rosecrans said. "No scale on this dern map," he snapped. "Jim, can you tell us how far from Murfreesboro their units are?"

"Yes, sir. 'Deed I can. Paced it off. I cackalated from the edge of town to the first unit astride the Nashville Pike by the railroad is a mite shy of two miles. It's a little hilly along the river. Through the cedars they're thick. Their lines'll go four miles if they'll go an inch."

"How about their positions?" Rosecrans asked. "What can you tell us about them?"

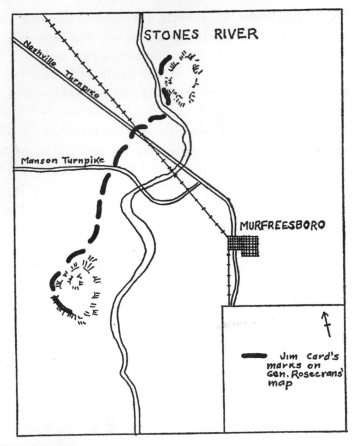

"Well, Gen'l, even the foxes of the fields have holes," Jim replied.

"What kind of shape would you say the Confederates are in?" Rosecrans asked. His voice was crowded with anxiety.

The spy's iron-gray brows knitted. "Devilish spirit, Gen'l. They are going to give you the battle of yo' life."

Rosecrans gulped his whiskey. When he put his glass down he said, "Anything else, Jim? This is wonderful."

"No, Gen'l."

Rosecrans grabbed Jim Card's hand. "Sheridan," Rosecrans said, "give this man anything he wants."

"Thankee, Gen'l. All I crave is a hoss to get me south over those long miles," Jim said. "I don't want any 'U.S.' brand on it, neither, 'cause I'm going to visit a patch farmer behind Bragg's lines and his cavalry goes ridin' about." Card smiled at Phil. "I want to thank you, sir, for giving old Jim Card his chance." He bowed to Phil then said to him, "I'll be in tech with you further, sir. I have the strongest faith that I will."

Rosecrans looked at Phil. "Can you take care of his horse?"

"Yes, sir. With the deepest of pleasure." Phil felt as if he were beginning to talk like the spy.

The day after Christmas General Rosecrans gave the order, and forty thousand of his soldiers marched in three parallel columns toward the Confederates at Murfreesboro, Tennessee. No sooner had the march started than Confederate cavalry under "Fightin' Joe" Wheeler attacked. Wheeler, and heavy rains, delayed the blue columns. The marching was hard.

It was almost the end of the year when the Union force moved into battle facing the Confederates. Phil's division took place in the right center of the line. The two armies were in cedar country, approximately a half-mile apart. The Confederates were on the positions exactly as described by Jim Card.

But the Confederates surprised the Union force. The gray-clad army attacked with the fury of madmen. Rosecrans expected the enemy to stay on defense. *He* expected to attack.

Through the cedar thickets charged the Confederates, straight at the Yankees. The blood-curdling Rebel Yell sounded above the artillery. The Southerners smashed the right of Rosecrans' line and rolled it up. Phil's division fought for its life. He sent Rienzi to the rear and ran up and down his embattled line, sword in one hand, pistol in the other. He saw Rebels break through the divisions on his right and left. "We must fire faster!" Phil screamed. "You people aren't working!"

The fighting raged at close quarters. It was worse than Perryville. Not only were the Confederates firing the fearful canister, but cannon balls from their guns bounded along the ground, thinning the blue ranks.

Phil saw four officers from his division streak for the rear. Phil swore. He tried to stop them but couldn't. They vanished in the cedars. Phil was furious with himself because he did not shoot them.

Phil sprinted to Colonel Fred Schaefer's regiment, for it seemed to be ready to break. Just as Phil arrived at the colonel's side, Schaefer was shot. Phil had a sinking feeling, but only for a moment. It was too turbulent a time to think long about the dead.

A mounted staff officer tore up and shouted at Phil, "General Rosecrans presents his compliments. He says for you to hold at all costs. He's rearranging the lines."

Phil felt he would have to die fighting. It appeared

that his division must be sacrificed. He ran along the line giving Rosecrans' message to the officers. When he arrived at Colonel George W. Roberts' regiment, he found him dead. Phil hunted for a Colonel Harrington.

"You are second in command of the Twenty-seventh, aren't you?" Phil shouted.

"Yes, sir."

Phil started to explain the situation to Colonel Harrington, and Harrington was shot dead.

Even with the loss of key leaders, Phil's division held.

An hour passed. The fighting did not lessen. General Rosecrans and part of his staff rode up to encourage the men. With them was Rosecrans' chief of staff, Colonel Garesché. "Great work, Sheridan," Rosecrans said.

A cannon ball plowed into the group, taking off Colonel Garesché's head and wounding two orderlies. Rosecrans' eyes widened in horror. His ruddy face turned white. He shook his head unbelievingly. He wheeled his horse and rode back. Phil ordered the wounded cared for.

The situation seemed impossible. Phil decided to counterattack. He gave the orders and charged with his men into the smoke. He was so excited he did not feel tired.

The Confederates reeled backward, but recovered and charged. Phil's division was not only in hand-to-hand combat, but it was almost surrounded. He received word that his men were running out of ammunition. Phil was shocked. He checked the nearest rifleman. The man had but two rounds. Phil tore to another company. The first soldier he asked had but one bullet. "Save it," Phil screamed. He sent two officers on the run to Rosecrans to demand ammunition.

Phil's division looked as though it were gone. He gave the order to fall back to the Manson Turnpike—to take up another position.

At seven in the evening the fighting died down. Phil and his men were exhausted and hungry. They had been fighting all day. Phil asked for a report. It was sad. He had lost over sixteen hundred killed and wounded. At night he slept under the protecting branches of a fallen oak. He dreamed he talked to Terrill, and they were friends.

Extra ammunition arrived in the morning. There was more hand-to-hand fighting.

At midnight Rosecrans called for a council of war. His headquarters were in a large Negro cabin. Rain beat a tattoo on the roof. The fire in the fireplace and two coal oil lanterns furnished the only light. Officers who had fought alongside their troops were dirty, their faces smeared with black powder. The scene looked unreal.

The conference reminded Phil of the report by the young scout, Mr. Hanna Aldine, on the affair at Munford-ville; some officers wanted to withdraw, some did not.

Rosecrans said it was vital that the enemy be kept from the Nashville Turnpike. "They get our supply line and we are gone," Rosecrans said.

Rosecrans turned to General George Thomas. "What do you think, Thomas?"

Thomas, a burly figure, looked like a fierce old lion. His bushy brown hair and white, pointed beard were black with powder. His beetle-like brows frowned. He took a long time answering General Rosecrans. Finally Thomas stood. The firelight played on his rugged features. "Gentlemen," he said, "I know of no place better to die than right here."

There was silence—only the pounding of the rain. Rosecrans said, "What about you, Sheridan?"

Phil jumped up. "I think we should attack at daybreak. My division has ammunition now. I request we be given the honor of leading the attack, sir."

Raindrops hissed in the fire.

Rosecrans gave an attack order, but the attack was not a vigorous one. The next day the two armies were exhausted, too tired to do anything but fight skirmishes and lick their wounds.

The battle was a tactical victory for the Confederates. No troops had ever fought harder. But in a few days General Bragg retreated south.

Jim Card, the Bible-carrying spy, had given accurate information of the Confederate positions in front of Murfreesboro. "The only trouble was," Phil muttered to himself, "we didn't act quickly or hard enough." He was disgusted.

Phil rode Rienzi back to the surgeons' tents to thank the wounded. On the way, he saw soldiers on grave-digging details piling the dead along the fence rows. The losses were staggering, and here was the frightful evidence. The demands on Phil during the last three days made him feel as if he were a hundred years old.

Back at his headquarters near the Manson Turnpike, an adjutant general told Phil that the four officers who deserted their companies in the battle had returned. "They've been investigated," the adjutant general said, "and they offered no excuse."

Phil ordered the division formed in a hollow square. The four cowards were paraded in the center. Four drummer boys took their places, one behind each deserter.

Phil marched into the square with his Negro servant, Zeb Marion. They faced the four officers. The regiments presented arms, saluting Phil. He returned the salute with his sword, and the muskets crashed to the order.

Phil handed Zeb a pocket knife. "Zeb," Phil said, "I want you to march to those four men and bring me their swords. Then you go back and cut off their officers' insignia."

Zeb took a step backward. "Sho'ly, Gen'ral! You mean for *me* to do that? Supposin' dey hits me?"

"If they hit you, Zeb, I will shoot them dead."

After Zeb performed his task the ranks opened and the drummer boys tapped their drums and marched the four officers out of camp.

The next day, January 2, 1863, the field telegraph bore news from Washington. President Lincoln had freed the slaves in the states fighting against the Union. Phil thought it over. It seemed to be a smart move, for slaves represented power and wealth in the South. He warned his quartermaster, "It won't be long before you'll have the problem of feeding Negroes who come over to our side."

Old General Rosecrans did not move all spring, for he wanted to build up his army. When he did, in late

June, march the forty miles south to Tullahoma, Tennessee, Phil wished he had information about the Confederates from Jim Card. But the tract-Bible-carrying spy had gone farther south, into Confederate country, to Chickamauga.

CHAPTER 14

Jim Card—Spy

MAJOR GENERAL WILLIAM S. ROSECRANS snapped the two-star epaulets on the shoulders of Phil's uniform and said to the generals lined up at the far end of the room, "All right, everyone—*right, face!* Now come by here and congratulate Major General Sheridan."

The senior officers filed by like kindergarten children. They pumped Phil's hand and uttered such things as, "Nice going"; "You earned it, congratulations"; "I hope I'm around when you get your third star."

Phil beamed. It was a tremendous day. He wished his father, mother, and Mr. McNanly could be present to see the new bright-blue and silver epaulets. He would write his parents, but no one knew where the old teacher had gone.

"Phil," General Rosecrans boomed, "it's a good thing you wear a moustache. If you didn't, you might be mistaken for an impostor. You must be the youngest major general on either side."

Phil could think of nothing to say.

Old General Thomas said, "But, Gen'l, if Phil ever needs any testy-monials about his ability to fight, I know where he can get one. From the Rebels!"

The room rocked with laughter.

"Now with the sweet comes the bitter," Rosecrans said. "Here it is. I want you gentlemen at this conference to know I'm being deluged with telegrams and letters, and I sit up nights listening to messengers from President Lincoln and Phil's *friend*, 'Old Brains.' " Rosecrans coated "friend" with icicles. Phil did not like General Rosecrans' belittling General Halleck.

Rosecrans wrinkled his nose and continued, "Halleck possibly is a good man. He didn't get his nickname, 'Old Brains,' by accident. I'd just like to see some old brains in his messages. I want you to know that I'm sending word back to those desk hounds in Washington that if we take our sixty thousand men into that wild, desolate, unfamiliar, hazardous mountain country in south Tennessee and northern Georgia we risk annihilation."

The room was silent. Phil agreed with Rosecrans, but he bristled over the insult to General Halleck.

"And what do I keep receiving?" Rosecrans said excitedly. "Nagging messages suggesting that we go south. One arrived an hour ago. It said that if we march into the mountains after Bragg we'll take the pressure off General Grant over at Vicksburg. All who believe that by risking ambush we'll help Grant, over on the Mississippi River, hold your hands up."

No one moved.

"We march into those mountains, we can be trapped,"

Rosecrans said. "Even the dumbest private knows that. But I warn you—be ready."

Phil rested his division, and when his men showed signs of restlessness he took them on all-day field exercises and made them solve advance-guard and rear-guard problems.

One evening, after he had eaten with a company of his soldiers at a camp kitchen, he rode Rienzi about the camp. It was twilight. The sun had disappeared behind a purple ridge.

Smoke from the kitchens shrouded hundreds of little tents and drifted slowly by the two wall tents Phil used as home and office. Here and there a flash of flame highlighted the scene. At the edge of camp a baseball game broke up because of lack of light. A quartet sang:

> Hail to the chief who in tri-umph ad-vances!
> Hon-or'd and blest be the ev-er-green pine!
> Long may the tree in his ban-ner that glanc-es
> Flour-ish the shel-ter and grace of our line!

When Phil swung out of the saddle at his tents, Zeb Marion, his Negro servant, grabbed the bridle.

Zeb's shoulders quivered. "I had a real fright, Gen'ral. I was settin' here whittlin' and thinkin'. Thinkin' how lucky it is that de colored folks everywhere kin now work for money, like I do. Suddenly, dat preacher-man eases around de corner of de tent like a hant. He burst out, 'Boy, git me de Gen'ral!' I didn't know him from Adam's off ox. I believes in de policy of dis army as you explained it, to win and all dat, but, Gen'ral, tell dis spy-preacher to make hisself known."

"Where is he now, Zeb?"

"Settin' in yo headquarters tent, waitin'."

The wiry little spy bounced up when Phil entered. Jim Card stuck out his hand. "Glad to see you, Gen'l. Came back to report."

On the table, grease ran down the sides of a candlestick made from a broken, angular bayonet. In the flickering light Jim Card justified Zeb's description. He was wild-looking. He had not shaved in over a month and his iron-gray whiskers made his face seem dirty.

After Phil welcomed him, Jim Card said, "I allus aim to bring you the truth, Gen'l Sheridan, for the truth shall make you free. Only trouble is, I don't have enough of it. I gave Bibles away to the Confederates in the tangled-up Chickamauga Creek country, but they move around up and down like foxes. You ever been down there, Gen'l?"

"No. I wish I had."

"Indescriable. Just indescriable. Untamed wilderness. Lookout Mountain and Missionary Ridge. I like that name. They rise up for thousands of feet, pillars of the Lord. The place is swarmin' with Confederates. They are also campin' in the mountains. Where, I don't know. I couldn't begin to cackalate 'em. But I stood almost as close to Gen'l Bragg as I am to you."

"What kind of man is he?" Phil leaned forward. This was the general they would have to defeat.

"Dyspeptic as all get-out. Testy even after dinner. Tall, awkward as a colt. West Pint eddicated. Hard as nails on his men, and he ain't exactly pop'lar. He's got eyes like yours, Gen'l. Can bore clean through a body."

"You had a difficult time fixing Bragg's strength and location?"

"Yessiree, but I have folks workin' to hep. Old Obadiah Throckmorton—mildest-mannered man that ever cut a throat or blew up a marshal's office—he's riding his mule in the Chickamauga Creek country. He's got a boy, Nelson, who's practically reliable. Nelson works in the Chattanooga telegraph office, eight and ten hours a stretch. They depend on him. He says the Rebs get in their troop-rations and practically everything else over the Nashville and Chattanooga."

"Jim, this is marvelous."

The spy shifted from one foot to another. "It's my bounden duty, sir, but I have somepin to ask. I'd like some other job, behind their lines, till things cool a spell. From their view I'm allus appearin' and disappearin'. That mought not be healthy."

"I see. Hmmm." Phil twisted an end of his black moustache. He studied Jim Card. He admired this daredevil.

"I'm not afeard, Gen'l, of stickin' my head in the noose, just want to postpone it." The spy laughed his hollow laugh.

Phil pulled a map from his leather dispatch case and spread it where it would catch the candlelight.

"What do you think of this, Jim? Do you think you can organize a group of your friends for a different mission? A small group. What I want is for you to go down to Bridgeport and Stevenson, on the Tennessee River, and set fire to the railroad bridges there." Phil placed his finger on the two towns. "They're not far from Chattanooga."

The spy's dark eyes gleamed. He answered instantly, " 'In flaming fire take vengeance.' Yes, sir, I'll do it. It's done, sir. I promise." Card held up his hand.

"It won't be easy, Jim. They will have guards at both bridges."

The spy seemed not to hear. He gazed at the ridgepole as if he expected to find the answer up there. "I been hankerin' to see a battle, but I can put that aside. I'll leave tonight and gather up some East Tennesseers and head for those bridges. They are loyal people, my mountain folk. I think I'll leave my brother, Esau—he's the youngest—with you, Gen'l. You mought need me. If you do, send Esau for me."

"I'll be glad to have him, Jim."

"You'll be happy to have him, sir. Everybody is."

"I am giving you a big problem, Jim. It won't be easy. Do you need anything?"

"Only matches, Gen'l."

Six days later the lieutenant colonel in charge of the outpost around Phil's camp rode his horse up to Phil's headquarters tent, dismounted and saluted. "Sir," he said to Phil, "our picket out on the Oak Grove road has stopped seven mountaineers—characters. They are armed to the teeth. The chief of the gang says he knows you and wants to see you. Our picket won't let 'em in. What shall I do?"

"What's the name of the head of the gang?"

"Jim Card, sir."

Phil and the lieutenant colonel rode out on the dusty

road to the farthest outpost. In the shade of a huge oak
sat Jim Card and the men he had rounded up to set fire
to the Nashville and Chattanooga Railroad bridges. Jim
Card, wearing a homemade sword fashioned from a scythe
with a corncob handle wired to it, stood up and grinned
when he saw Phil. Jim brought a young-looking boy up.
Phil judged him to be about eighteen.

"Gen'l Sheridan, sir, this is Esau, the best of the Cards.
I am leavin' him with you. You need me, send Esau.
He'll fetch me." Jim Card turned. "Esau," he said, "you
mind your P's and Q's."

Esau grinned at Phil. He craned his long neck and
bowed. Esau, clean-shaven and pink-cheeked, looked
fifteen years younger than the spy.

Phil shook hands with each of the mountaineers. In
their careless dress and black slouch hats they looked like
land pirates. No two were armed alike. They had single-
barrel shotguns and a British muzzle-loading caliber .557
Enfield. One carried a Colt five-shot revolver. Another
had a dagger with a Spanish religious figure for a hilt,
and one had a rusty U.S. Navy cutlass.

Phil pulled out his caliber .44 Rogers and Spencer and
a handful of bullets. "You'll need a pistol, Jim," he said.
He looked over the group anxiously. "Do you think you
have enough men?"

" 'Deed I do, Gen'l. On a burnin' expedition the main
thing is to have a small, likely group you kin trust. I
been raised with these fellows since childhood." The spy's
eyes moistened.

Jim Card kissed his brother Esau good-bye, and the
mountaineers disappeared in the underbrush. Phil helped

the slender boy onto the back of Rienzi, and the big animal carried double back to camp.

Time dragged. General Rosecrans could not make up his mind to march his army into the mountainous country ahead.

There was no news of the bridge-burning expedition. Phil began to worry.

Zeb Marion was concerned with Esau and he gave Phil a good report on the young mountaineer. "Fine boy— pleasant and quiet. He heps shine yo 'quipment, sir, den he hops to de kitchens to chop wood. De mess sergeant down at Company 'A' of the Twenty-second Illinois say Esau's worth any two men he's got. I tell you, Gen'l, I like him a heap better'n his Bible-totin', sweet-talkin' brother."

Suddenly the situation changed. General Rosecrans decided that he did not want the bridge over the Tennessee River at Bridgeport burned. He gave Phil the job of riding at the head of cavalry thirty miles across country to seize it. Phil worried for fear that Jim Card had already burned it.

When Phil and his raiders arrived at the bridge, they captured part of the Confederate guard, but the rest of the Confederates managed to set fire to the wooden trestle. Phil questioned a captured lieutenant and his men. They had never heard of Jim Card, and Phil believed they were telling the truth. *Where has Jim Card gone?* Phil asked himself on the ride back. It was a mystery.

To pass the time, Phil invited General George Thomas to take a train trip to see a bridge Phil's men had built over a creek. It was a twenty-mile ride. The old, lionlike general and Phil seated themselves on the dirty, cane-bottom seats of a day coach. Although the train was scheduled to move, it did not turn a wheel. Phil was embarrassed. When the conductor walked by, Phil snapped, "When are you going to start?"

The conductor, six feet tall, tugged at the lapel of his dirty blue coat. "When I get good and ready," he said.

Phil burned. General Thomas gave no sign that he was irritated.

After fifteen minutes, the conductor walked through the car again. Phil grabbed the conductor's coat and swung him around.

"Move this train!" Phil barked. His face purpled. The veins in his neck stood out.

"I take orders only from my superiors," the conductor said.

Phil jumped into the aisle. He smashed the conductor a blow in the face, kicked him in the shins, and when the conductor ran out of the car rained blows on his back. Phil chased the man off the train and stalked back to the car. He reached for the cord overhead and yanked it twice. The engine rang its bell, jerked the cars, and wheezed on its way. Phil took his seat beside the elderly general. "I'm the conductor on this trip," he said.

Thomas nodded his hairy head but did not reply.

When Phil and General Thomas were returning, they had a short wait until the engine was ready. At the far edge of the wooden platform a group of Phil's soldiers were arguing with a news peddler. It looked as if there might be a fight. Phil shoved his way into the group. "What's the matter?" he demanded.

"This news-butch is a robber, sir," a soldier said. "He's charging us a dollar for Cincinnati newspapers and ninety cents for a plug of common chewing tobacco."

"Is that right?" Phil shouted at the peddler.

"Well, General, it cost me—"

Phil charged the peddler and banged the man's head against a railroad coach.

"Stop!" the peddler cried. "I'll reduce prices!"

On the train riding back to camp, Phil felt low. *I told Bill Terrill I had control of my temper,* he said to himself. *I have a long way to go.*

When Phil and General Thomas dismounted from the train at Phil's camp, they found all the tents down. The wagon train had pulled up beside the kitchens. The bustle of the breakup of camp sounded like a hive of angry bees. Both generals wondered what the matter was.

Phil's adjutant general saluted. "Sir, orders from General Rosecrans. We're marching south in an hour."

Phil's heart jumped. He knew the hazards ahead. He liked to fight, but he did not relish marching into the wild Cumberland Mountains. Clearly, the mountains favored the defenders. Phil felt a burning desire to win.

General Thomas shook Phil's hand before he mounted his horse to return to his own camp. "The time has come," the old general said. "Phil, I'm glad we have a fighter like you on our side."

When Thomas rode away, Esau Card came up. He bowed his long neck forward. "Sir, I heerd that on that raid you went on t'other day you looked but found nary a trace of my brother Jim."

"That's right, Esau. I wish I knew where he was. We could use him right now."

Esau's pink face clouded. "He must have run afoul of trouble. I want to go look for him."

A staff officer rode up, dismounted, and saluted Phil. "Sir, how far back do you want the ammunition wagons?"

"Just a minute," Phil said. He turned back to the boy. "Yes, Esau, I think you had better go. You might be able to help your brother. If you find him—*when* you find him, rather—tell him we're headin' south. Do you want a horse?"

"No, sir."

Rosecrans' army inched into the mountains. Every man in it expected ambush. Phil and his division had a particularly hard job: the rear guard.

Confederate horsemen kept tabs on the Union army. The gray-clad riders did not dash in and fight. They watched. At night, sometimes, Phil and his men could hear Confederate bugles. It was a most unpleasant, haunting sound.

There was a cavalry raid far to the rear to stop the Union supplies, but each day Rosecrans' army marched deeper into Confederate country. Phil worried more than his men, for he knew more than they did. Rosecrans was moving on a fifty-mile front, his army divided into three parts. Phil knew that if the Confederates attacked hard they could defeat the Union army in detail before the widespread parts could help each other.

Two weeks after Esau left, Jim Card walked down the side of a forest-covered mountain and waited along the roadside until Phil rode by. When Phil saw Jim Card,

he vaulted from Rienzi's back. The spy looked older—
much thinner. His eyes seemed to be on fire. "They caught
Esau and hung him, Gen'l." The spy's shoulders sagged.
"I loved that boy."

"What!" said Phil. "Who?"

"Bushwhackers. They're agin both sides. They're fighting everybody. The scum of the earth. I know who done
it, and I'm roundin' up thirty East Tennesseers. 'I will
render vengeance to mine enemies.'" Card shook his fist
at Phil as if he were an enemy.

"I am terribly sorry, Jim. We all loved Esau." Phil
looked at the spy's tattered clothing. "Why, Jim, you've—"

"Been in prison," Jim finished. "We couldn't burn the
bridges. They caught us at night, skiftin' across the river.
Two of the boys were shot outright. The rest, I dunno.
They carried me to Chattanooga and penned me up. It
was annoying. They were fixin' to have me stand trial,
but I managed to shift a bar in the window and skinned
out."

"Goodness!" exclaimed Phil. "What a time you had!"

"When I got out," Jim said, "I thought I ought to
walk the chalk, but I stayed and visited about. Can I
see yo' map?"

The spy wet his stub of a pencil and ringed an area
around Lafayette, Georgia, near Chickamauga Creek.
"Bragg's army," Jim said.

Phil's eyes bulged. If Bragg was there, the Union
columns were in danger.

"And I got more news," Jim said. "I hunted up Obadiah
Throckmorton's boy, Nelson. He's on our side. Nelson's
assistant operator in the Chattanooga railroad station.

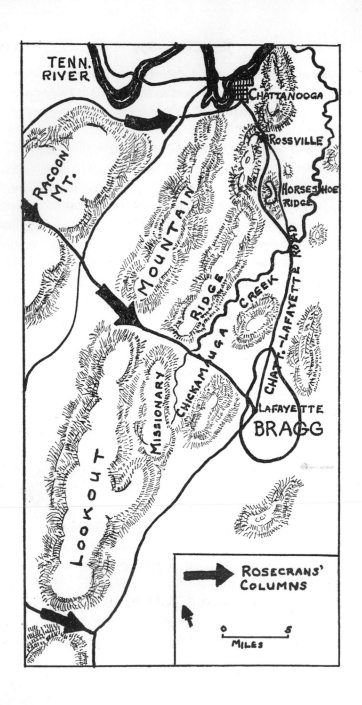

TENN.
RIVER

CHATTANOOGA

ROSSVILLE

RACOON MT.

HORSESHOE RIDGE

MOUNTAIN

RIDGE

CHICKAMAUGA CREEK

CHATT.-LAFAYETTE ROAD

MISSIONARY

LAFAYETTE

BRAGG

LOOKOUT

ROSECRANS'
COLUMNS

0   5
MILES

His daddy couldn't spell 'madam' either forward or backard, but Nelson's different. He tuck to telegraphin' like a boy to vacation. He kin listen-read the telegraph as fast as they can send it. Nelson told me—that was two days ago—that reinforcements are comin' for Mr. Reb."

"How many?" Phil was breathless.

"Dunno. Gen'l Lee, up in Virginia, is sendin' Gen'l Longstreet's army and a fighter named Hood by rail to Chattanooga. How many in an army?"

Phil hesitated. He knew he could trust the spy, but what about an assistant telegraph operator in Chattanooga? Was the information good? Phil remembered his first meeting with John Hood long ago at West Point. Phil had taken over forty dragoons from Hood in Pitt River Indian country. *Now it is either Hood or me*, Phil thought.

The soldiers tramped by. They liked their general and spoke to him. "You haven't seen that conductor lately, have you, General?" one asked, and all the men in ear-shot laughed.

Phil grinned, but his mind was on the important news from Jim Card.

"You gave me a pistol once, Gen'l," Jim Card said, "but I didn't keep it long. Have you another you can spare me? Mought have use for it."

Phil handed Jim his pistol. "This is a good one," Phil said.

Jim Card checked its load. A strange look came into his eyes. "Vengeance is mine, I will repay," he vowed. Then he turned and walked up the mountain.

CHAPTER 15

Defeat at Chickamauga;
Out of the Trap at
Missionary Ridge

G ENERAL ROSECRANS was worried and looked it. The very earth seemed against him. Tremendous Lookout Mountain, and beyond that Missionary Ridge, frowned on his army. The two earth forms dominated the country. The only information he had about the enemy came from Jim Card and a handful of cavalry scouts. They said General Bragg and his fighting Confederates were waiting for the Yankees at Lafayette, Georgia.

Rosecrans ordered a midnight council of war, and among those "invited" was young Phil Sheridan.

General Rosecrans paced the floor of the house serving as his headquarters. He stopped, perched on a table, whipped a rosary out of his pocket and twirled it about a forefinger. The day before, September 19, 1863, bitter fighting had occurred. Every officer at the war council was tired. General Thomas, propped up in a corner of the room, was asleep.

Rosecrans spun the rosary about his finger, then untwined it. Every few minutes he asked the same question, "What is the best thing for us to do?" Phil's emotions were mixed. He was sorry for the general, but worried. Lives of Union soldiers hinged on the conference, and here was the leader, unstrung.

The army commander spied Thomas asleep. Rosecrans barked, "General Thomas, what about you?"

Old Thomas sat up and rubbed his eyes. "Oh, yes," he said, "yes—yes indeed."

"Yes indeed what?" Rosecrans half-shouted; then he took the sting out of his voice and said, "What do you think we should do, General?"

Thomas took a deep breath. "I say, strengthen the left." He smoothed his bushy hair and stretched. "You know, Gen'l Rosecrans, I served as a young shavetail in Bragg's batt'ry in the Mexican War. In Mexico he wasn't cautious. They say he's waitin' for us. That's lucky. He could have ambushed us or beat us separately."

Rosecrans fingered the rosary. His eyes were the eyes of a man who thought the odds against him were impossible. He mumbled something about criticism.

It was an unhappy conference. It was two in the morning when it ended. Phil, along with an aide, walked Rienzi through the woods to his bivouac. There was a touch of fall in the night air. The woods smelled fresh, as they often do at night. Phil was dog-tired. *Fateful days,* he thought. *Men on both sides fighting as hard as they can. What peaceful woods—but tomorrow?* Rienzi stumbled and Phil jerked the horse's head up. *We must win. Rosecrans?* Phil shook his head.

"Halt! Dismount! Who goes there?" cried a sentinel.

Phil and the aide-de-camp pulled hard on the reins and swung out of their saddles. They knew they were at the outpost of Phil's division. You had to be cautious with a sentinel at night. The great Confederate leader, General Stonewall Jackson, was killed by his own men at night through error.

"General officer and aide," Phil replied.

"Advance one to be recognized," demanded the sentinel.

"Stay here," Phil said to his aide. Phil led Rienzi forward in the darkness.

"*Halt!*" shouted the sentinel. He peered into Phil's face. The soldier had his bayonet pointed at Phil's stomach. Then he said, in a lower tone, "Give the countersign."

"Fort Henry," whispered Phil.

"Hello, General," said the sentry, lowering his bayonet. "Come on in."

Half an hour later Phil, with his saddle for a pillow, curled up under a pine.

The next day the battle continued. The two armies tore at each other between the Chattanooga-Lafayette Road and Chickamauga Creek. The fighting was the hardest Phil had yet seen. The crash of the fight sounded for miles.

Suddenly Rosecrans, or one of his staff, made a mistake. One of his divisions was ordered to leave its position in the thick of the fight and to pull back.

Longstreet's Confederates howled through the gap. In the front were Texans under General John Hood, Phil's classmate. The Confederates rolled up the Union line and split it. Phil swore—and prayed. His division

was cut off. It looked like the end. Rosecrans and some
of his senior generals rode hastily back to Chattanooga.
The confusion in the Union army angered Phil. He was
disgusted and frightened.

General Thomas grouped his corps of men on Horseshoe Ridge and saved the Union army from disaster. They
fought off hundreds of Confederates.

Phil gathered most of his division and led them toward
Rossville. Then he turned his men around on another
road and marched to the aid of General Thomas on the
embattled ridge.

When Phil found the old lion, Horseshoe Ridge was
under severe attack. General Thomas, dressed as usual
for battle in his best uniform, stood a hundred yards back
up the ridge from his men. The two lines were not over
forty yards apart. The Confederates knew that only
Thomas and his men stood between them and a smashing
victory. The Confederates charged again and again. Their
red battle flags waved in the midst of the fight.

Phil approached the dignified, heroic-looking General
Thomas. Phil saluted. "General," he said, "I have most
of my division a short way back. How can we help?" A
cannon ball plowed the dirt at their feet.

General Thomas brushed the dust off the sleeve of
his uniform.

"Pretty bad, isn't it?" Phil said.

For a few moments, Phil thought Thomas was not going
to reply. Then Thomas said, "It'd be wrong to attack.
Help us hold on. When it's dark, cover our move back
to Rossville and Chickamauga."

That night the Union army, cooped up in Chattanooga,

was choked with gloom. When Rosecrans' staff officers
totaled up the dead, wounded, and missing, they reached
a figure of sixteen thousand. Phil felt as if the bottom had
dropped out of the universe.

No one knew how many men the Confederates had
lost. A captured lieutenant said to Phil, "Our brave General
Hood lost a leg." But Phil could only be sorry for his
own losses and the defeat.

The entire North grieved. The papers blamed the
casualties on President Lincoln. The only glory in the
battle was the stand of General George H. Thomas and
his men. "The Rock of Chickamauga," they nicknamed
the strapping general.

Siege warfare started. Chattanooga was in turmoil.
Officers ordered trenches dug across lawns and streets.
Soldiers moved into private homes. Confederate cavalry
cut the supply line to the city, and soon Rosecrans' army
was on starvation rations.

A few supplies trickled in on a winding, narrow trail—
"The Cracker Line," the soldiers called it. For want of
forage, mules and horses began to die. The Bluecoats in
ranks began to think they might be next. Every military
man in the city worried; the Confederates fortified the
top of Missionary Ridge.

Phil refused to depend on the Cracker Line. To feed
his hungry men he sent Captain Thickstun, of Kentucky
cavalry, north across the river to collect and bring in food.

Jim Card walked into Phil's headquarters in the
beleaguered city. Seeing Card in such a troubled time was
like having reinforcements arrive.

Card handed Phil his pistol. Three notches were carved

in its handle. "I missed the battle, Gen'l," Jim said. Then he caught Phil's eyes on the notches. "I got the ring-leaders," Jim drawled, "but it don't bring back Esau."

To get Card's mind off his brother and to learn about the country, Phil questioned him. When Phil was through, Card said, "I find you're short of eatin'-rations. Gen'l, I kin hep you."

After listening to Jim Card, Phil sent him across the river to assist Captain Thickstun. Soon corn, chickens, turkeys, ducks, eggs, and grain rolled in on wagons. Phil had a secret supply line. "Beats the Cracker Line," Phil's men said, but the rest of Rosecrans' army was starving.

One day when Phil was riding the outpost line under the brow of Missionary Ridge, he stopped to talk to soldiers in a rifle pit. The Confederates were a half mile up, on the top. A man on a sorrel horse rode up from the rear. He wore a Union Army private's blouse, with no insignia of rank. His beard and hair were nut brown. He carried neither sword nor pistol. He sat his horse as if he had been born on it. Something about the man seemed familiar. Phil wondered who he was.

The stranger reined his horse about five yards from Phil. "General Sheridan?" he asked.

"Yes," Phil said.

"Don't know if you recall me. I met you down at the landing at Shiloh. My name is Grant."

Phil's eyes widened. "Why, General Grant!" Phil tickled Rienzi with a spur, rode up to the general, took off his flat black hat, and stuck out his hand. "I want to congratulate you, sir, on your victory at Vicksburg."

"Thank you," said Grant. He squinted at the top of

the ridge. "I just relieved Rosecrans. President Lincoln—
he sent me. Phil, what do we have to do to get this army
out of the hole and beat those fellows up there?"

Grant's manner was self-reliant. He looked perfectly
at ease.

"We have to feed it, sir. That's first."

"You're right," Grant said.

Five days later General Grant put troops across the
river. A pontoon bridge was built, and a new road became
available. Food, hay, and grain rolled into the city. The
Union soldiers were thankful. "Cracker Line's open!"
they shouted when the first supplies arrived. "Full rations,
boys!"

Reinforcements arrived in Chattanooga. Hank Slocum,
wearing the two stars of a major general, hunted up Phil.
At first Phil did not recognize his former roommate, the
boy who long ago helped Phil in his studies at West Point.
Hank Slocum had lost hair, he wore a beard, and he was
thinner.

"You look different," Phil said.

"I ought to," Hank replied. "I was wounded at Bull
Run. I had other rough days. Second Bull Run—I hate
the name—Antietam, Fredericksburg, Chancellorsville,
and Gettysburg. Terrible names, Phil, terrible!"

The two friends chatted a half-hour. Phil told Hank
all he knew of the situation they faced.

"I believe General Grant can get us out of this fix,"
Hank said.

"I do, too," Phil answered.

In a little over a month Grant formed his army under
the brow of the massive, forest-covered ridge. The Con-

federates on top could not depress their cannons enough to bear on the Union forces almost directly under them. On signal, the two-mile-long Union army marched forward and upward. General Grant's plan was to seize the first line of Confederate fire pits, reorganize, then go to the top. Another Union force would swing around and cut off the Confederates.

Sixty Union color bearers led the way up Missionary Ridge. The Stars and Stripes whipping out in the breeze inspired Phil and thousands of others who marched upward. Confederates killed many color bearers. Other Union soldiers picked up the flags. Sheets of fire cut down men in the blue ranks. The echoes thundered in the valleys. The Union soldiers did not stop in the first line of trenches. They couldn't. Confederate rifle fire was too accurate. They charged to the top. Phil scrambled to the front of his division. After a wild battle, the Confederates broke ranks and ran off the ridge to the south.

Phil was excited. As soon as he recovered his breath he raised his head and shouted, "Oh, God, who art the author of peace and lover of concord!" To his men he screamed, "Come on!"

Other Union officers on the ridge were satisfied, but not Phil. He yelled orders. He wanted pursuit to make the victory complete, and he wanted it at once. He feared the Confederate army might escape. Phil's men formed an advance guard, and shortly they captured almost as many prisoners as men they had lost in the charge up the slope: two thousand. Phil became angry because generals close by were not interested in pursuing. Most of Bragg's army escaped.

At twilight the moon came up, a red disk. The forest below looked like a series of ghostly ridges. Jim Card, in from Phil's private supply line, hunted Phil and found him on top of the ridge. The spy perched on the barrel of a captured Confederate cannon. He looked like a chipmunk. The moonlight softened the spy's whiskers and made the barrel of the gun gleam.

"I saw the charge up the ridge," the spy said. "While I was climbing up a little while ago they were still toting the wounded down."

"I'm glad you saw a winning battle," Phil said. "I want to thank you for all you've done. You're invaluable. To win it takes the work of many people."

"No man is an island, no man stands alone," Jim Card said.

"What's that?" Phil said. He was tired, but the sentence made him alert.

Jim repeated it. "John Donne said that, Gen'l, and he knew considerable about the Good Book." Jim fumbled in his knapsack and handed Phil a piece of paper. "I like that word so much I wrote it down. You can have it."

Phil repeated: "No man is an island, no man stands alone," then he stuck the paper absent-mindedly in the leather dispatch case, and slung it over his shoulder. "I thank you," he said.

The moonlight made entrancing shadows on the red earth. It was amazing that so beautiful a night could follow such a day of torment. After a while Jim said, "I'm going back to colportering, sir."

"What do you mean?"

"I guess your next move will be south after Mr. Reb, won't it, Gen'l?"

"I don't know the plans, Jim."

"I'm guessin' you'll be heading south. They say Gen'l Grant ain't likely to let this army stay still. I don't know the country any more south than right here." Jim tapped the cannon. "When I lost Esau it took the starch out of me. I'm headin' back to East Tennessee to deliver Bibles and tracts." Jim nodded toward his knapsack. "It's my callin'."

Phil gave the spy every argument he could think of, but Jim shook his head. "I've had all I kin stummick. I'll pray for you, your soldiers, and the Pres-i-dent every night. And, Gen'l, remember Jim Card hepped a little. He and the cap'n let you eat manna in the desert like our fathers. That was my best chapter."

Phil hoisted the spy's knapsack on his shoulders and walked with him to the place where a trail ducked down the ridge to the city. Phil hated to tell Jim good-bye. He wondered if he would ever see Jim Card again.

When the two friends parted, Jim Card saluted, and Phil returned the salute. "It's the first time I ever did that," Jim said, "and the last."

A month later Phil had even harder good-byes to say. General Grant had been called to Washington for a third star and was promoted to general-in-chief of the Union Army. He telegraphed for Phil to join him in Washington. Phil was sorry to leave. Bigger problems, he knew, were in the East, and also dangerous politics. He was not confident of the future. He was afraid he would become a staff officer. "I'll tell General Grant I want to be a combat leader," he said.

When General Thomas told Phil good-bye, Thomas said, "I have word you are to command the cavalry for the Army of the Potomac, Phil."

"Cavalry?"

"Yep. You can do it. I expect to hear you're successful," the grizzled general said as he shook Phil's hand.

When Phil caught the train for Washington, every man and officer in his division marched to the station. Phil dashed into the telegraph office to find Nelson Throckmorton, the young telegrapher who had helped him.

"He's gone west," the station agent said. "Left me short-handed, too."

When Phil climbed aboard the last coach, Zeb Marion shook his hand. "Jest checked on Rienzi," Zeb said. "He's right comfortable in the stall dey fixed in dat boxcar. Lots of hay. I'm sure goin' to miss dat horse and you."

The engine sent up clouds of smoke. On the platform of the last car, Phil turned to make a speech. The words stuck in his throat. His officers and men, grouped on a nearby hillside, took off their hats and yelled. It was a cheer Phil never forgot. It thrilled him to the core. The whistle tooted and the bell rang. The engine chuffed and jerked the cars forward. Phil waved his little black hat, but he could hardly see his men.

CHAPTER 16

The Snapping Turtle

T HE train swayed its way through the Great Smokies and up into Tennessee. Cinders drifted into the rickety wooden coaches. Phil's car was crowded with wounded and with soldiers going home on leave.

He tried to think of the problems ahead. He knew politics appointed officers above the rank of captain, that there had been failures in the high command of the Army of the Potomac. He worried. He had never been to Washington and he knew only two people, Generals Grant and Halleck, and neither was a real chum.

"You are going to command the cavalry of the Army of the Potomac, Phil," General Thomas had said. Meade was the commanding general of that army. They said General Meade was hard to serve under.

Phil thought about cavalry. He believed that the generals on the Union side were not using it smartly. He hoped General Meade would give him free rein.

When the train finally chugged into Washington, Phil made arrangements for Rienzi, then took a buggy for Willard's Hotel. The *clop-clop* of the horse's hoofs on the macadam street was music. It was April 4, 1864.

He was thrilled to catch a view of the capital, but the crowds on the street seemed to be unaware that a terrible war was on. And at Willard's Hotel the two-deep throng of staff officers, paymasters, adjutant generals, quartermasters, and judge advocates at the bar angered him. He wondered when they worked. It was four-thirty in the afternoon.

The desk clerk gazed at Phil's scrawl on the ledger, then at Phil. It was hard for the clerk to realize that this little, red-necked, scrawny officer, whose uniform collar was three sizes too large, was the famous General Phil Sheridan.

Phil cleaned up, pulled on his best blue uniform and took a hack to the War Department. The sight of the odd-looking brownstone building made him unhappy. He wished he were back with General Thomas.

When General Halleck caught sight of Phil he rushed out of his office and pumped Phil's hand. "Why, Sheridan! Glad to see you. This is fine. Come in, come in. Your success at Missionary Ridge—I was so happy to read the reports. I knew all the time you were a leader."

Phil beamed. He liked General Halleck.

Halleck lifted the front of his uniform coat and tugged out a gold watch. "I think we can still catch the Secretary."

A sleepy sergeant sitting outside the door marked SECRETARY OF WAR rose to his feet. He was the oldest sergeant Phil had ever seen. He decided the sergeant must be a veteran of the Mexican War.

"Mr. Secretary," Halleck bowed, "this is Major General Philip H. Sheridan."

Secretary Stanton half rose from behind his rolltop desk, shook hands limply, and sank back in his swivel chair and frowned. He was about Phil's size but fat. Phil felt as if he had shaken hands with a corpse. Mr. Stanton peered through his steel-rimmed spectacles. "Humph!" he said.

Phil felt the Secretary disapproved.

"When did you arrive?" Stanton said to Phil.

"Two hours ago, sir. No, it was three."

The Secretary turned his swivel chair slightly. "When will General Grant be back in town, General Halleck?"

"Tomorrow afternoon, sir." Halleck scratched his elbows. "Sir, General Sheridan just arrived from—"

"Yes, yes, I know," interrupted the Secretary irritably. He said to Phil, "How's General Thomas?"

Phil seized his opening. He talked of General Thomas' stand at Horseshoe Ridge, and of how his men loved him. But Secretary Edwin Stanton seemed not to be listening. He appeared to be sizing Phil up. Phil shifted in his chair.

Mr. Stanton twisted a finger in his unusually long gray beard. "Halleck, you'd better get Sheridan out of here and over to the White House. The President left word he wanted to meet him. I have some papers to work on."

The President! Phil's pulse quickened.

"I just want to say," Halleck said as he and Phil stood up, "that General Sheridan is a winning general."

"Hope so," said the Secretary. He frowned and swept his hand fussily over a heap of papers. "You'll have to excuse me, gentlemen, I have important work."

President Lincoln stood over a foot taller than Phil. When Halleck introduced Phil, the President clasped Phil's hand in both of his. "This is a real pleasure," the President said in his soft voice, his homely face breaking into a tired smile. "I want to thank you, General Sheridan, for all you've done. Sit down, please. I'm glad to talk to a fighter. All I've done today is talk to people who want to be generals. Most of 'em want to start at the top and work down. If a man came in here and said he wanted to be a private, I wouldn't know what to do."

Phil chuckled and relaxed. He had heard that President Lincoln was a great storyteller, but the President said, "General Sheridan, please tell me how to win the war."

Phil's mouth dropped open. "Sir, I—I—" he sputtered. "I don't know exactly."

"You're unique," the President said. "General Grant says he is placing you in command of the cavalry of the Army of the Potomac. About twelve thousand men and horses—right, General Halleck?"

"Yes, sir. Including twelve batteries of horse artillery. Men from Michigan, Ohio, New York, Pennsylvania, Massachusetts, New Jersey, Indiana, Vermont, Connecticut, and from the Regular Army."

The President clasped his hands behind his head. His long arms, bending at a sharp angle, made him seem awkward even though he was seated. "General Sheridan," he said, "I hope you can put some of your fire into the cavalry. It hasn't been handled well at all. Do you think so, Halleck?"

"No, sir."

The President stood, and Phil realized the interview was over. "Cavalry," the President said with a wide grin, "whoever saw a dead cavalryman?"

Phil burned inwardly and labored not to show it. He had

heard that remark before and he did not like it. He knew the President meant that usually the cavalry was sent to the rear as soon as a fight started.

Phil said, "I'm not boasting, sir, I haven't seen my command, but I think the cavalry will pay off."

The President smiled. "I know it will," he said.

That night Phil hardly slept. The noise from the bar, floating up to his room, kept him awake until after midnight. He blazed again over President Lincoln's remark, "Whoever saw a dead cavalryman?" *The Army of the Potomac.* Its commander was General Meade—"the snapping turtle," the young officers called him.

Phil felt he would meet a problem in General Meade. General Grant would be easy to work for. All you had to do was your job. But Meade? And Meade stood between him and Grant.

Phil thought over everything he had heard about "the snapping turtle." A West Pointer from Pennsylvania. Old as the hills—seven years older than General Grant, even older than Thomas—and as mean as the dickens. They said Meade was irritable even in his sleep. He was brave. He had been wounded at White Oak Swamp in the Peninsular Campaign of '62. The great battle of Gettysburg had been won by Meade, but he let Lee and his Confederates escape. People said that General Meade's subordinates were afraid of him. Phil pounded the bed and said aloud, "Well, I am not afraid of George Meade."

On the train to Culpeper Court House the next day, General Grant sat on the dirty green plush seat beside Phil and touched a match to a cigar. It was pleasant watching the rolling Virginia countryside. Phil was thrilled to be with the general-in-chief. Phil stole a look at the firm mouth and the slender fingers on the cigar. He thought of the long chances Grant had taken. The armchair generals counted Grant out at Vicksburg, but he had won a great victory, cutting the Confederacy in two and blocking supplies and reinforcements from Texas.

Grant blew a smoke ring. "Seventy-three good miles to Culpeper," he said. "The best advice I've received in this war by far came from Sherman. He telegraphed me, 'For goodness' sakes, get your headquarters out of Washington.'" Grant chuckled. "I hate humbug, and in Washington I'd be forever defending my orders." He shivered. "I certainly admire the President. Impossible job."

Phil wished again that he were to fight directly under General Grant rather than Meade.

"Nice horse you have up ahead," Grant said.

Phil told the general how Captain Campbell of the Wolverines had given him the big black. Then Phil told about the raid at Booneville, Mississippi. How his Michigan cavalry had ridden behind the Confederate lines and had ripped up track and burned coaches of the Mobile and Ohio Railroad. Grant listened closely.

"That's how I think cavalry should operate," Phil finished.

The train stopped so the engine could obtain water. Negro soldiers guarding the train stepped off and stretched their legs. Soft white blossoms of swamp magnolia laced the green woods. Warm fragrant air drifted through the open windows. Virginia in the spring was beautiful.

When the train rattled on, Grant said, "You'd better tell your ideas on cavalry to General Meade."

At Brandy Station the train stopped so that Phil and Rienzi could get off. Phil wound a red sash about his waist, hooked on his sword, and tucked a pair of new buckskin gauntlets in his sash. Grant shook his hand. "I'm counting on you, Phil," he said. "I brought you here because this army needs your fire and dash. I'll keep in touch with you."

Phil felt nervous riding Rienzi down the road to the cluster of circus tents serving as Meade's headquarters. His mind was on General Meade.

Outside the center tent of Meade's headquarters, which sported a gaudy pennant bearing two stars, a sentry in Zouave costume—baggy red trousers, white gaiters, bobtailed blue jacket, and a red pillbox cap—banged his rifle with its fixed bayonet to *present arms* when Phil dismounted. Another Zouave ran up and took Rienzi. Phil was not impressed with the Zouaves. They did not look like fighters to him. A flock of high-ranking officers about the tents peered at Phil curiously.

Meade stood behind his desk when Phil marched in, halted, saluted, and said, "Sir, Major General Sheridan reports to General Meade for duty, as ordered."

Meade's hooked nose, cold blue eyes, whiskers, and wan smile made Phil think of an old bloodhound. The army commander stood six feet tall and his uniform hung on him. "Sit down, Sheridan," he rasped.

After a few pleasantries Meade said, "We have twelve thousand horsemen who'll be looking to you for guidance, Sheridan. In about two weeks General Grant is sending us into the Wilderness after Lee." Meade ran a finger around the inside of his four-inch-high starched collar. "This army must give a better account of itself in the Wilderness than it has done in the past. It will." Meade's jaw clamped shut. The lines around his mouth pointed down. He *did* look like a snapping turtle.

"You'll find you have some good generals," Meade continued. "Jim Wilson, Gregg, Torbert, Davies, Merritt, and a lad named Custer."

"Custer? I've heard of him."

"Devil-may-care fighter. My Volunteer Aide, Colonel Lyman, says Custer looks like a circus rider gone mad." Meade smiled faintly. "You'll see his costume. Fiery young man."

"What kind of shape are the horses in, sir?"

"The snapping turtle" bit the air. "Our cavalry kills off horseflesh faster than we can supply it." He crossed one leg over the other, and his amazingly large jackboots, which looked like boots a pirate might wear, bulged forward at the knee. "The cavalry thinks there is only one pace—the gallop. This is true whether they are on patrols, courier duty, or guarding wagon trains. I want that stopped."

Phil took a deep breath. "General Meade, I have ideas on cavalry and I would like to explain them."

"So?" The old Spartan frowned.

Phil plunged ahead. "Take the Confederate cavalry, General. In '62, Jeb Stuart rode around the Union Army. He did great damage. The information he took back helped Lee and Stonewall Jackson to win the Second Battle of Bull Run. Then, last October, Stuart circled the Union Army again. His raid into Pennsylvania was brilliant. The Union cavalry rode after him in circles. It was on the defensive. Take the Confederate cavalry general, Nathan Bedford Forrest. His raids penalized Rosecrans. John Hunt Mor-

gan, 'The Rebel Raider,' has captured fifteen thousand
Union soldiers. When he raided into Ohio, he—"

"The snapping turtle" stood up. He interrupted, "I don't
want to hear any more about it."

Phil jumped up. He slapped his gauntlets against his
leg. "General Meade, let me help this army."

"What do you want to do?"

"Sir, when we go into the Wilderness, I want to lead the
advance.

"Cavalry can't fight."

Phil glared up at the elderly man. "I'll teach it to fight,
sir."

"How?"

"By the time we go into action I'll have every man
trained to dismount on command or signal. Every fourth
man'll be a horseholder. He'll take care of his horse and
the horses of the three men nearest to him. The horseholders will lead the horses to the rear or into a ravine, out
of danger. The men who are free of their horses will fight
on foot."

"Those tactics may be all right against Indians, in Indian
country, Sheridan. Here, all the cavalrymen want to do is
gallop their horses."

"I'll change that. They'll become fighters."

Meade sat bolt upright in his camp chair. His eyes looked
dreary. They were underlined by dark half-circles. He
stroked his pointed beard. Finally he said, "I don't think
your ideas will work at all, but I'll try them just one time.
When we march south, put ten thousand of your troopers
out to the flanks as screens, but see that two thousand of
your best men and four batteries of artillery guard our

wagon trains. Remember, they carry our supplies and without supplies you do not fight long. Keep the wagon trains in mind. Confederate cavalry has our trains on its mind, I can tell you, sir."

Phil left. He had won his first skirmish with General Meade, but he felt as though Meade missed the point he was trying to make.

In the camps about Brandy Station, Phil inspected his cavalry. The horses were skin and bones. He increased their feed and ordered rest. He sent staff officers to obtain more animals. He made his men pretend they were mounted, and taught them to "dismount and fight on foot." He held target practice for his soldiers with their Sharp's carbines, which fired a heavy fifty-two caliber bullet accurately six hundred yards and which gave the users great fire power.

General Meade came to see a review of Phil's horsemen. Meade seemed unimpressed when the lines of cavalrymen and artillerymen swept by. When he left Meade said to Phil, "Remember, protect those wagon trains."

Most of Phil's horsemen rode out to protect the flanks when the Army of the Potomac started south. The Wilderness was a tangle of thickets, briar patches, forests, and swamps. Its streams seemed to run toward every point of the compass. The roads and trails crisscrossed. They were hard to follow. There was a blind, confusing fight. Great numbers were killed. In the space of a day, the eight miles from Old Wilderness Tavern to Todd's Tavern became a dreadful outdoor hospital for both the Blue and Gray Armies.

In the middle of the battle, Phil received a message from

General Meade: . . . *You had better draw in your cavalry so as to secure the protection of the trains.*

Phil was angry. He cursed. He ordered his cavalry to the rear. His ammunition wagons were now leading his unit and they ran into sixteen thousand Union soldiers under Major General G. K. Warren. Phil's wagons and artillery blocked Warren's infantry. The two lines of horsemen and infantrymen squeezed by each other, but slowly. When the cavalry wagons and the infantry wagon train met head-on, traffic came to a standstill.

Warren and Phil argued. "I'm just carrying out the orders," Phil said.

In two hours Phil received a message to report to General Meade.

"The snapping turtle" was furious. When Phil walked into the big tent Meade did not greet him, nor did he return Phil's salute.

"Sheridan," Meade rasped, "your damned cavalry blocked Warren's Corps and made them late for the battle."

"You changed the orders," Phil said loudly, "and it was not smart."

Meade stepped back. No one had talked to him that way for over twenty years. "You are insubordinate." He leveled a finger at Phil. "You did not carry out your orders."

Phil replied, "I told you I want to use cavalry to whip the enemy. You want to use it as train guards. That's entirely wrong."

Meade recovered his composure slightly. "You tell me. What were your wagons doing on that road? You blocked it."

Phil lost his temper. He put as much acid as he could

into his reply. "Those were my ammunition wagons. It is customary for troops going into a fight to have reserve ammunition. You should know that. A horse and a man can carry only so much."

"I blame you for the confusion," Meade said tartly. "You did not protect the flanks."

"I blame you," Phil snapped. "Your orders caused the snarl."

Meade's head jerked up. "Hmmm," he said. He made a visible effort to control himself. "We are getting nowhere talking like this. If my orders caused the trouble, I apologize."

But Phil did not relax. He said, "You give me a chance. I'll take my cavalry behind the enemy lines and whip Jeb Stuart."

"Orderly!" Meade howled and, before the soldier could appear, he shouted, "Get my horse!" To Phil he said, "Return to your command, sir, and get it straightened out. I am going to report you to General Grant."

Phil was lonely on the ride back to his bivouac. He wished he had not lost his temper. He wondered what Grant would do.

Two of Phil's young tigers galloped up—Brigadier General Custer and Colonel Ranald Mackenzie. Mackenzie, trim and lean in his tight-fitting regulation blouse, had been wounded five times since First Bull Run. Custer wore a theatrical, wide-brimmed black hat, a shiny cotton-velvet blue jacket, a flowing red necktie, and a large star on each shoulder. His blond ringlets fell almost to his epaulets. He yanked on the reins and his white horse reared and pawed the air. Custer tugged at his tight black velvet trousers, which wrinkled at the knee.

He whipped out his saber and saluted Phil with a flourish, and said, "Sir, Mackenzie and I want to know if we're going to be allowed to fight? We can lick those Confederates."

Mackenzie said, "General, the wagon train is straightened out. My artillerymen are disappointed they did not fire a round."

Phil's worries vanished. With fighters like these he would succeed, if he received another chance.

General Grant sat under an oak studying a map and smoking a cigar when General Meade rode up. Meade dismounted stiffly.

Grant looked up. "Hello, Meade," he said pleasantly. "I was just going to send word to you that I think we can slip around the Confederate right, toward Spotsylvania Court House."

"Yes, sir." Meade bit off his words. "I came to tell you that General Sheridan's handling of the cavalry has been amateurish and that he has been insubordinate."

Grant sent up a puff of smoke.

Meade continued, "He said if he were given the chance he could ride behind the enemy lines and whip Stuart's cavalry."

Grant looked keenly at Meade. "Did he say that?"

"Yes, sir."

Grant flicked the ash off his cigar and said, "Then let him try."

CHAPTER 17

Raid at Yellow Tavern

PHIL turned in his saddle. The May sunshine, the green countryside, the sky, and the purple violets along the gray fence rails were lost on him. He thought, *Where is the enemy cavalry?*

From the distance came the rumble of guns. A signal sergeant, riding behind Phil, said, "Those guns are back at Spotsylvania Court House, ain't they, General?"

Phil nodded. He did not wish to get into conversation with the sergeant. He had other things to think about. A sign tacked to a fence post read: SIXTY MILES TO RICHMOND.

The rear part of Custer's advance guard up ahead was galloping. Phil instructed a staff officer, "Present my compliments to General Custer and tell him I want his column to walk. We are not out to kill horses."

The signal sergeant said, "Sir, General. The men back of us are cussin' Rienzi. He's so big and walks so fast all of us have to slow trot to keep up."

Six Union soldiers galloped in from the east. The patrol

leader, a corporal, touched his forage cap to Phil. "Sir, I report. We went down that road four miles. No enemy."

The column jingled on. The signal sergeant said, "We're after the most valorous man in the Confederacy."

"What's 'valorous'?" a private said.

"Brave," the signal sergeant said. "I mean Stuart."

Phil remembered the day at West Point when James Birdseye McPherson introduced him to Jeb Stuart. Even then Stuart was a husky, but his weak-looking chin did not serve notice that he would be a hero of the South.

A private said, "I hear Jeb dresses fancy. Hat with a star, plume, and all. Jackboots, cape, and red saddle blanket."

"He doesn't wear a red saddle blanket," the sergeant said. "His horse does."

The soldiers laughed. A sparrow hawk darted at the column, then veered off. "I guess Uncle Jeb is the best fighter in the South," a private said. "A real ledgun."

In the morning there was no reveille, but Phil's cavalrymen were up before daybreak. Horses were watered and fed. After a hasty breakfast the raiders splashed across the Ta River. Just then Stuart's cavalry rode in like a whirlwind and struck the rear guard. The attack sounded as if it were close. Phil thought, *Let the rear guard handle that.* He raised his fist above this head and pumped his hand up and down. The main body of raiders saw the signal and urged their horses into a trot. Phil and his men rode deeper into the Confederacy.

When they splashed across the North Anna River, Phil ordered the Richmond and Fredericksburg Railroad bridge set on fire. In twenty minutes he turned in the saddle. A tower of black smoke was a beacon signaling the presence of his raiders.

Rifle fire cracked out up in front. Phil's glasses let him see the tail end of the advance guard jump from their horses. He halted the main body. Shortly, a horseman galloped back and reported to Phil, "Rebels ahead at Beaver Dam Station. Lots of 'em. General Custer said to tell you, sir, he's fighting on foot."

"Thank you," Phil said. He sent stronger patrols out to his flanks.

When Custer chased the Confederates away from the railroad station, Phil rode up to it. Wounded from both sides were being treated in a grove across the street, and four hundred Union soldiers who had been prisoners of the Confederates, and who had been set free by Custer, were cheering. Rienzi shied as Phil dismounted. Phil stalked into the empty railroad station. The telegraph instrument was clicking. "Get me an operator," Phil said to an aide.

A Union sergeant reported.

"Can you work this key?" Phil asked.

"Yes, sir."

The telegraph instrument stopped chattering.

Phil wrote on a piece of paper and handed it to the sergeant. "Send this," Phil said.

In a moment the sergeant clicked off Phil's message: SPECIAL FOR RICHMOND FROM BEAVER DAM. SEND THREE TRAINS HERE AT ONCE. UNION CAVALRY DEFEATED, BUT WE ARE OUT OF AMMUNITION OF ALL TYPES. NEED MANY CARS FOR PRISONERS AND WOUNDED—GENERAL J. E. B. STUART.

Twenty minutes later, back came the answer: TWO TRAINS LEAVING FOR YOU AT ONCE FROM HANOVER JUNC- TION. THIRD TRAIN WILL DEPART FROM RICHMOND IN ONE HOUR.

Phil laughed. He called for George Custer and said, "Get ready to ambush these two trains."

There was confusion in the village of Beaver Dam as Custer called off the advance guard formation and pre- pared the ambush. Men ran to their positions. The artillery was hidden. In a half hour the two incoming trains whistled for Beaver Dam Station. The first train was captured easily, but then someone set fire to the railroad station. The build- ing burned rapidly. The engineer of the second train saw the blaze, slammed on his brakes, and backtracked at full speed. Phil laughed when he saw the captured ammuni- tion on the first train, but cursed when he saw the second train escape. "I'll court-martial the man who set fire to the damned station," he said, "if I ever find out who did it."

After tearing up ten miles of track and burning the cap- tured train, Phil ordered General Custer to set fire to a supply dump in the town. It contained enough food to feed Lee's Army for twenty days. Phil sent messages to Grant and Meade. He was happy.

The next morning his raiders were in the saddle at day- break. They had hardly warmed up their horses when one of Custer's staff officers dashed up. His horse pranced while he gave Phil his report. The animal danced in the road, ears back, eyes wild. "Sir, they are blocking the road ahead."

"How many?"

"About four thousand."

Phil said, "Put out a new advance guard and we'll take the Negro foot-road. We won't stop. We'll push on toward Richmond."

More messengers came, and they all said about the same thing: "General Stuart is galloping his cavalry hard to cut us off at Yellow Tavern. They may strike us in the rear, too."

Phil felt the pressure. About eleven thousand men depended on his decisions. He trotted up a hill. The fighting was in the flat below. Over the tops of the trees you could see the buildings of Richmond, six miles away. It was a temptation to cut for the city. But if he captured the city thousands would die. "We couldn't hold it," Phil muttered.

Explosions jarring the hill made him concentrate on the field below. He was at Yellow Tavern.

Phil galloped to find his hard-fighting artilleryman, Colonel Mackenzie. "Bear down on targets around Yellow Tavern," Phil said.

The artillery horses, six to a gun and six to an ammunition caisson, dashed in to the edge of the woods, and the cannoneers unlimbered. They sprang from the backs of the horses, unhooked the guns, and turned them toward the Confederates. The cannoneers loaded the guns in a twinkling. The horses were led to safety. The guns roared, and the batteries were covered with black smoke. A black cloud floated over the field. But through it you could see that horses were down.

Phil sent for Custer.

When Custer vaulted from his horse, he was on fire

with excitement. He touched the rim of his wide black hat to Phil. "Command me, General."

"Charge their artillery," Phil said. "Smash it. You cut them up and we will win."

Custer's long nose went up. His eyes narrowed. "Sabers or pistols?"

"The pistol attack."

"Can the band play, sir?" Custer pushed nervously at the curls at the back of his neck.

"The band?" Phil started to say, "No, you'll need the bandsmen as litter bearers for the wounded." Instead, he said flatly, "No."

Custer's bluecoats trotted out of the woods and formed two lines, thirty yards apart. They looked splendid, as if they were on parade. Every forty yards a guidon fluttered. Custer rode in the center of the front rank, red necktie streaming over his shoulder. He drew his saber and pointed at the enemy.

When the cavalrymen were fifty yards out of the forest, Union bugles sounded the charge. The riders screamed. It was blood-curdling. The horsemen bent low over the necks of their mounts as they pounded for the Confederate artillery. Pistols were extended. The wind tore at the faces of the riders. The Confederates fired. Horses fell. But most of the Union riders raced on, unharmed. They tore straight for the Confederate cannons. The Confederate batteries bellowed. Custer raced ahead. Pistols cracked.

Confederate cannoneers fell. Some abandoned their guns before the fury of the charge, and ran for the rear. Others surrendered. Riderless horses bucked aimlessly about. A smoke cloud drifted back and hid the batteries. For the first time since he wore stars, Phil wished it were his job to ride in front of the men.

In a few minutes, a courier dashed back to Phil. "General Sheridan," he said, "the Confederates carried off General Jeb Stuart, badly wounded."

Phil's heart jumped. He felt happy, and at the same time sad. "Are you sure?" he said.

"Saw him myself," the trooper said. "He got it in the stomach. They put him in an ambulance toward Richmond."

Four days later, Phil bought the Richmond *Inquirer* from two newsboys. The paper told of the death of the great Confederate cavalryman. Phil knew Stuart's loss would hurt the South far more than the damage of the raid.

Phil guided his column to the east around Richmond, and not far from Petersburg he obtained supplies from the Union General Butler. Sheridan finally brought his men back to General Meade's headquarters. He was proud. They had been behind the enemy lines for sixteen days and had ridden one hundred and fifty miles.

When Phil Sheridan strutted into Meade's headquarters, the old "snapping turtle" stood behind his makeshift desk of two planks thrown across sawhorses. Meade shoved out his hand. "I'm delighted and proud of what you did, Phil," he said. "Great."

Phil Sheridan grinned. Neither he nor Meade was anxious to talk about their last meeting.

Phil appreciated Meade's manner. He was in a happy mood, but he did not know what to say.

General Meade held out a Richmond newspaper. "They're making quite a hero of General Stuart."

Phil read the quote from Robert E. Lee, "Stuart never gave me false information. He was second to none in valor, zeal, and devotion to his country."

" 'Devotion to his country,' " Phil said. "That's what makes 'em hard to beat."

"That and General Lee," Meade said dryly.

When Phil reported to General Grant, Grant laughed. "Phil, where on earth have you been?" Grant's blue eyes shone. He draped an arm across Phil's wide shoulders. He made Phil feel seven feet tall.

Grant's determination showed in his face. "How are your horses?" he said.

"Good, sir, except fifteen of my buckos gave their mounts all the cold water they could drink yesterday, when they were overheated, and they died. They'll pay for those fifteen horses next payday."

Grant lit a cigar. "Get ready to fight," he said. "I want you to lead the advance and find out 'zactly where Lee's Army is. Head in the general direction of Cold Harbor."

Phil had never heard of the place. As soon as he could he looked it up. Cold Harbor. The place had an evil, fateful sound.

CHAPTER 18

"Too Young for the Job"

W HEN Phil's cavalrymen marched south down the
lonely roads, he saw from the map why General
Grant mentioned Cold Harbor. Whoever held the place
controlled the roads for miles. But there was an obstacle
to worry about: Custer's scouts reported Confederates
were already there.

The dust, kicked up by Phil's horses and churned by
his artillery and trains, filtered above the treetops. There
was no escape from it. Each man wore a handkerchief over
his nose and mouth, and men and animals sneezed.

The signal sergeant riding behind Phil said, "Sir,
General, this dust is a signal that we're coming, like that
railroad bridge we burnt on the Yellow Tavern Raid."

The column halted while the advance guard probed
for Confederate pickets.

Phil rode forward and found Brigadier General Gregg
talking to a captured Confederate. A Union cavalryman,
up the road twenty yards, tightened his saddle girth and
sang:

We'll rally 'round the flag, boys,
We'll rally once again,
Shouting the battle cry of freedom!

General Dave Gregg, a former Regular Army Indian
fighter, said to Phil, "The Rebs have blocked the road at
Haw's Station. Here's one we flushed. Custer wanted to
charge, but I ordered him to dismount and fight on foot.
Charging breastworks . . . " Gregg shrugged. A band up
front played "The Dashing White Sergeant."

"That's Custer's," Gregg said. "He's encouraging his
men."

Phil looked at the captured Confederate private. "Who's
your leader?"

The Virginian looked up insolently. He tucked his
thumbs inside his brass "C.S.A." belt buckle, leaned back
against an oak, and said, "Who wants to know?"

Phil boiled, but he held his temper. He swung out
of the saddle and stepped to the Confederate. The Virginian looked unconcerned. He fanned himself with his
black hat.

Phil grinned. "Have a drink of water," he said to
the prisoner, and he unhooked his canteen from his saddle
and passed it to the private. The Confederate took a deep
swig, wiped his mouth on his shirt sleeve, and said,
"Thank you, suh."

"I'm General Sheridan." Phil jerked his head toward
the sound of the rifle fire and band music. "I'd like to have
the honor of knowing whom I'm fighting."

General Meade's aide, Colonel Ted Lyman, rode up
and listened.

The Confederate prisoner relaxed. "Sir, you're fightin' a fire-eater from South Carolina, Gen'l Wade Hampton. He tuck Jeb Stuart's place. Wade's all right, 'cept he enjoys fightin'. He thinks war's a game."

"How far is it to Richmond?" Phil asked.

"Fifteen miles, sir."

"How many men do you have?"

The Confederate placed his hand on the little black frying pan tied to his belt. "I've told you all I can, Gen'l. If I tole you more, couldn't live with myself."

Colonel Ted Lyman said, "The thing that troubles me, General Sheridan, is that it is not a gain to kill off these brave people. I've seen Southerners now for over a year. They're too brave to be lost. The whole war amounts to a national insanity."

Phil did not reply.

In an hour the road was cleared of Confederates. Phil trotted ahead to congratulate Custer, but Custer was up with the point of the advance guard. Phil's advance guard went into action again. This time the Confederates had more men. Phil studied the situation. A cannon ball smashed into an oak, making a crash as though two freight engines had collided. A spray of splinters covered him.

Phil sent two divisions across country to hit the Confederates from the flank, and the men in gray retreated. There was a lull while Phil's skirmishers covered the area. In a little while he realized he was in command of Cold Harbor. It was a dreary crossroad settlement, a few houses in the pine woods.

A Union band played "The Silver Bell Waltz" and "March and Quick Step" as Phil made his soldiers labor to improve the trenches left by the Confederates. When the band stopped, church bells sounded faintly. They were in Richmond. The piney woods seemed peaceful. Men sat on the top of the breastworks and smoked and rested. They were tired, but they did not relax long, for the enemy came back.

Robert E. Lee's infantry marched through the choking dust and hurled themselves at Phil's lines. The battle stopped for a while, then more Confederate fighters appeared. Phil saw that his cavalrymen were being outnumbered and could not hold long. He sent riders tearing to Mcade and Grant with messages: "Hurry up!" Phil worried. It seemed forever until Meade's advance guard appeared. One of the most tragic of American battles got under way.

When Meade's greater force finally arrived, Phil was able to pull his cavalrymen out of the line.

Phil and a friend took a quick swim in a stream, from the deck of a Union gunboat. When they were through they tossed their filthy uniforms overboard, and the captain of the warship gave them sailor uniforms for the walk back to camp. Down the road clattered U. S. Grant and some staff officers. Grant stopped his horse and grinned when he saw Phil dressed as a sailor. "Hello, Sheridan," he said. "Have you captured the Navy?"

Phil felt sheepish. He started to reply, but Grant said, "Get your cavalry ready. I may have a job for you." Then he trotted on.

Grant decided to smash the Confederates, who were now dug in behind breastworks. When his lines marched forward they were caught in fire from the flank as well as from the front. In eight minutes, seven thousand Union men were lost. It was slaughter. The blue lines reeled back, but when they attacked again they hit the Confederates in piecemeal fashion, and more men died. The Confederates stopped the suicide attacks easily.

When news of the Battle of Cold Harbor reached the North, headlines screamed:

GRANT A BUTCHER!
HE ACTS UNDER LINCOLN'S ORDERS
ELECT McCLELLAN PRESIDENT

Near the end of the battle, Phil received orders to report to General Grant. Phil wondered what was up. He found the Union leader sleeping in the shade of a scrub pine, on a board.

An *aide* saluted Phil. "Sir, General Grant said when you came for me to wake him up."

Grant sat up, rubbed his eyes, and bit off the end of a cigar. He looked younger, because his beard and moustache were trimmed. "Hello, Sheridan," he said. "Give me your map."

Phil crouched close by while Grant placed a finger on Charlottesville and moved it to Hanover Junction.

"It's sixty-five miles 'tween those places," Grant said, "or thereabouts. I want you to cut loose out of here and tear up track. Do you think you can rip up sixty-five miles worth?"

Phil was happy at the thought of leaving the stench of Cold Harbor, and he liked the idea of being on his

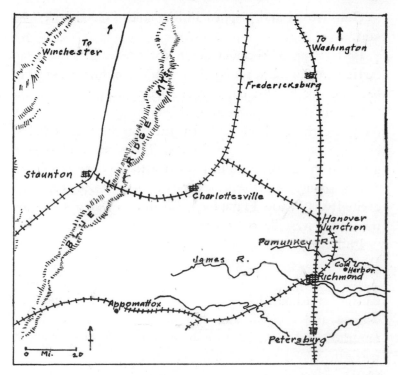

own, on a raid. He remembered later that he had said
"Yes" to General Grant's question in about five seconds.

"If you can wreck track 'tween these places, you'll put
a stop to supplies coming into Richmond from the Shenandoah," Grant said. "I'm giving you a pontoon train. They
carry their canvas boats and all in their wagons. They
can bridge a stream while you're thinkin' about it. And
I figger you'll need fightin' help, so I have a force coming
from the Shenandoah to meet you. You have about six
thousand horsemen. Right?"

"Yes, sir."

Grant stood and gripped Phil's hand. "Good luck," he said.

Phil stripped his men down for the raid. Each man carried one hundred rounds of ammunition. For the saddle-bags he ordered bacon, coffee, sugar, bologna, hardtack. "We can do without our blankets and ponchos in this May weather," Phil said. In the wagon train officers' baggage was cut to a minimum. The pack mules were given to the artillery to be loaded with extra ammunition.

No sooner had Phil started than a scout reported excitedly, "Wade Hampton's cavalry is going to strike us on the west flank, and they're racing to head us off."

Phil cursed. How did Hampton know about this raid? Was there a spy in Grant's headquarters like Jim Card?

At Trevilian Station the enemy blocked Phil's road. Custer attacked. He circled to the rear and captured wagons and Confederates. But on the next day Phil lost one thousand men. He tore up six miles of track, but that was all. Word came to him that the Union army which Grant was sending from the Shenandoah Valley would not arrive.

"We can't tear up track and fight, too," Phil told his generals. "We'll pull back to General Grant."

Phil felt disgraced. It was a long ride back.

Grant was undisturbed when he heard Phil's report. Phil could not possibly have accomplished his mission. "Take a rest," said the general-in-chief, "and get your cavalry ready to go again."

In July the news was bad. From Atlanta: Major General James Birdseye McPherson, the boy who graduated first in Phil's class, one of the most popular men in the Union

Army, had been shot off his horse and killed in the fight for the city. Also from Atlanta: General Sherman demanded reinforcements, and this embarrassed Washington and General Grant. From Washington: Confederates were at the outskirts. The hard-bitten Confederate fighter, General Early, had led his army out of the Shenandoah Valley and was almost at the capital. Then Jubal Early withdrew, but he raided Chambersburg, Pennsylvania, and demanded $100,000 from the town. When the citizens could not raise it, most of the town was set on fire. The pressure on President Lincoln and General Grant became greater.

August, 1864, was as dark. To Lincoln and Grant the war seemed almost won, but to the people who saw the names of loved ones and friends on the longer and longer casualty lists, the war seemed endless, impossible.

Grant traveled north. He wanted to study the Shenandoah situation. The Valley was Jubal Early's "home," and it supplied the Confederate Army and Richmond with food. The Union General Hunter, at the foot of the Valley along the Potomac, was so harassed by orders from Washington that he had no idea of where the Confederate Army was. Things were in a turmoil. General Grant wired for Phil Sheridan.

When Phil stepped off the special train which rushed him to the Monocacy River, a few miles east of Harper's Ferry, he expected to find Grant worried. If General Grant was, he did not show it.

The senior general took Phil into the dingy waiting room of the station. A Negro was sweeping the floor.

"This floor doesn't look bad," Grant said to the Negro. "We can excuse you."

"Thank you, Boss."

"Sheridan, how are you?" Grant said.

"Fine, sir."

Grant lit a cigar and cocked one leg over his knee. "Did you bring your horse?"

"No, sir."

Grant sent up a puff. His blue eyes fixed Phil. "You're going to need him."

Phil waited anxiously for Grant to tell him what was up.

"I'm giving you a big job, Phil. The Shenandoah Valley. The Confederates have been embarrassing us there, and *from* there, ever since the war started. For a long time it was Stonewall Jackson country. Now their general, Jubal Early, is also a tough fellow. Don't underestimate him a minute. He controls the Valley. It's an important place. It's a supply area for Lee's Army and Richmond. I want you to defeat the enemy. I want you to clean the Valley out so that crows flying over it for the balance of the season will have to carry their own rations. Make it a desert. Do not burn houses, but notify people to get out. All provisions and cattle should be used by you. Don't leave anything that will tempt the enemy to return."

Phil fanned himself with his flat black hat. The problem looked gigantic.

"Here's something you have to pay some mind to," Grant continued. "They have a Confederate Ranger in the Valley. I think he's in the Valley. He has caused us more trouble. We've hunted him, wasted troops which should have been elsewhere to try to catch him. It's been like chasin' a fox, or a will-o'-the-wisp. He appears, does his dirty work, then disappears. He and his Rangers kill couriers, staff officers, and raid headquarters. He must have a thousand spies. Operates at night. In the daytime he just melts away. His name is Mosby."

"What troops will I have, General?"

"You'll command an army—about thirty thousand. About eight thousand of it is cavalry. We're calling it the Army of the Shenandoah."

An army! Phil moistened his lips. He started thinking of the things he would do to make his army efficient. *Take Buell and Rosecrans*—Phil interrupted his own thoughts. "When do I start, sir?"

Grant smoked a while. He stroked his bearded chin. "I'll give you the word. In the meantime you can do a lot. Get ready."

"Sir, may I keep Generals Custer, Gregg, Merritt, that young artilleryman Mackenzie, and—"

"Keep all your leaders, Phil. Now here's something you ought to know." Grant hesitated a moment. "The President, and others in Washington, think you are too young for the job. I don't. I insisted the command of this army be given to you."

Phil's chest rose. He was determined not to disappoint his friend, General Grant.

"A lot depends on you, Phil," Grant said slowly. "If you do not do a good job, if Early whips you, Lincoln will not be re-elected this fall. If that happens the war might be stopped. If it is, the Union will never be together again. A lot hinges on you."

Phil felt as though a weight had been placed upon his shoulders, but he believed he could do what General Grant ordered.

I am not too young for the job, Phil vowed. *I can do it.*

CHAPTER 19

Into the Valley

IN HIS headquarters and about his camps, Phil worked to ready his army and to become acquainted with its key leaders. One of them, Major General William Emory, veteran of the Mexican War and a Regular Army cavalry-man of frontier service, graduated from West Point the year Phil was born.

But not all of Phil's officers were old. Second Lieutenant Meigs, engineer officer, one year out of West Point, seemed almost like a boy as he spread his maps on Phil's table. John Meigs had just returned with an engineer sergeant from behind the Confederate lines. John's long face shone in anticipation as he prepared to explain the fruit of his work to Phil.

"This map, sir, shows the extent of the Shenandoah Valley. My orders were to go no farther south than Strasburg. I got the lay of the mountains from a geography. I have a series of larger scale maps for you giving more detail. This is beautiful country, General. I'll always remember the clouds and shadows on the Blue Ridge. Hundreds of fine farms dot the floor of the Valley."

"Did you have any trouble with the enemy? Did you learn where he is?"

John Meigs brushed back a shock of brown hair from his forehead. "Some loyal farmers told us that Early's army is at Martinsburg. Sir, we tried to avoid people. You can go anywhere you wish in the Valley if you travel at night and stay off the roads. We mapped in the early morning hours and holed up at night."

Phil traced the Valley Pike from Harper's Ferry to Strasburg.

"A fine metal road," the young officer said. "Notice Massanutten Mountain, General. It'll make you think of Missionary Ridge."

"This is a tremendous job, Mr. Meigs. I thank you for what you've done. Thank your sergeant, too."

After Lieutenant Meigs had gone, an adjutant general handed a Phil a wire.

WAR DEPARTMENT, WASHINGTON
SEPTEMBER 15, 1864

MAJOR GENERAL PHILIP SHERIDAN

WHEN YOU MARCH SOUTH, MAKE CERTAIN THE ENEMY DOES NOT SLASH AT YOU THROUGH GAPS IN THE BLUE RIDGE. YOU MUST NOT FAIL.

EDWIN M. STANTON
SECRETARY OF WAR

Phil glared at the paper. The pressure was mounting. Almost every day he received some such telegram from the Secretary. Life seemed to be a succession of problems.

"Sir," the adjutant general continued, "General Crook is here on that spy business. He has a Negro with him,

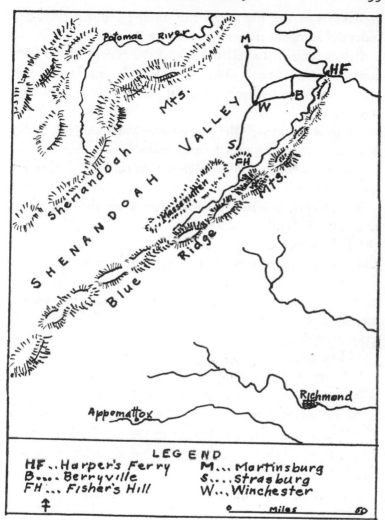

LEGEND

HF.. Harper's Ferry   M... Martinsburg
B.... Berryville   S.... Strasburg
FH... Fisher's Hill   W... Winchester

0 ————— Miles ————— 50

and down in the mess hall the hundred and fifty 'Confederate' Rangers are waiting for you."

It was difficult to tell the age of the Negro with Phil's
friend George Crook. The Negro's body was strong but
stooped. He had kinky, close-cut white hair, but young-
looking eyes .

"This is the man," Brigadier General Crook said, "who
will carry the messages to and from Winchester for us.
He says he knows Miss Rebecca Wright, the Quaker
schoolteacher."

The Negro bowed. "Knowed her since she was born,
sah. She's folks."

"This man," Crook continued, "says he can get by the
Confederate patrols between here and Winchester."

"Got a pass right here," the Negro said, holding up a
piece of paper. "Vegetable toter. I just drive my wagon
and dey never bothers me. I raised a lot of dem boys in
gray uniforms."

"How old are you?" Phil asked.

"Plenty old enough, Gen'l. Double grandchildren."
The Negro flashed a perfect set of white teeth.

"I am sure we can trust him," Crook said.

" 'Deed you can, sah. I want to see my people happy.
Dey's free, Father Abraham say, but de white folks in
the Valley don't cogitate it."

Phil wrote on a small piece of tissue paper:

September 15, 1864

I learn from General Crook that you are a loyal
lady and still love the old flag. Can you inform me
of the position of Early's forces, the number and

strength of his divisions, and his intentions? Are
any troops coming from Richmond?

I am, very respectfully, your most obedient
servant,

P. H. Sheridan, Major General, Commanding

Crook produced a small piece of tinfoil and wrapped
the message in it. The Negro popped the capsule in his
mouth and said, "She'll ride easy there."

When Crook and the Negro had gone, Phil and his
adjutant general walked down one of the steep streets
and into a stone building which served as a mess hall for
the staff. When the two officers walked in, a man wearing
the insignia of a major in the Confederate Army laid back
his head and bellowed, "Attention!" The musty-smelling
room was jammed with men in gray.

Phil stepped to the center of the room and said, "This
is the first time I have ever been in a roomful of
Confederates."

The only man to laugh was the adjutant general. The
men in the gray uniforms looked serious; some appeared
determined, others a bit frightened or perhaps confused.

The major in the Confederate uniform said, "Sir, we'll
have about seventy-five more volunteers tomorrow."

Phil held up a piece of paper. "I came here to read
this to you," he said. "It will give you an idea why I
asked for volunteers to wear Confederate uniforms. This
was written by a nine-monther before his enlistment was
up last week. Listen:

" 'I was getaway-man on a six-man horse patrol last
Wednesday, on the Berryville Road. It was hot and we
were careful not to use up our horses. Sergeant Fletcher

put one man out as a point and told me to hang back a good quarter. Along about five in the afternoon we come across a woman setting in a wagon with a broken axle. They all bunched up to help her. I was back in the woods on a little hill. Suddenly, out of the brush near the wagon came shots. Our men went down. Two horses struggled in the road. I hung there a minute and saw about fifty men, dressed like farmers, dash out to the wagon. I tore back to Harper's Ferry Outpost and gave our captain the news. The next day he took the whole company out there, and it was horrible. The five bodies lay in the ditch along with the two horses. Carbines, ammunition, shoes, saddles, and the three other horses were gone. The farm people nearby said they heard no shooting, knew nothing about our dead, and never heard tell of the woman with the broken axle.' "

Phil jammed the paper in his pocket. "Those murderers were one of two things," he shouted, "bushwhackers, or Mosby's men. Major Young!"

The sturdy "Confederate" in the front of the group stood at attention.

"I want you to divide these brave people into groups," Phil said. "Send some up the Valley several miles beyond Strasburg, others west of Martinsburg. I want a system rigged so that they can pass back information to me. When we go up the Valley—I don't know yet when that'll be— I want information as to who the loyal people are and where the enemy is. I take off my hat to this group. I love people who take chances."

A "Confederate" held up his hand. "Sir, I want to ask what Mosby looks like."

"Can you answer that, Major Young?" Phil said.

"I never saw him," the spy-leader said, "but he's a Virginian. Young, smooth-faced, skinny, and straight. Handsome. He was a lawyer before the war and puts out that he's a lieutenant colonel in command of the Forty-third Battalion of Virginia Cavalry."

The veins in Phil's neck swelled. He cried, "He's no more battalion commander than a goose. He doesn't come out and fight like a soldier. Mosby is a bushwhacker, pure and simple, and if he's caught"—Phil twisted an end of his black moustache—"he'll be treated as such."

Phil shook hands with each spy before they parted. It was a solemn moment. Each "Confederate" knew that capture in enemy uniform meant death—probably by hanging.

Phil was in bed a few nights later when General Crook knocked. "Sorry to bother you, Phil," George Crook said, "but you'll sleep better after you read this." George held out a piece of tissue paper to Phil. "This just came in by the old Negro."

Phil held the tissue near the candle.

September 16, 1864

I have no communication with the rebels, but will tell you what I know. The Confederate division under General Kershaw, and twelve guns of artillery, have been sent away and no more men are expected, as they cannot be spared in Richmond. I do not know how the troops are situated but their force is smaller than represented. I will take pleasure in learning all I can. The bearer may call again.

Phil's dark eyes glowed. He repeated softly, " 'Their force is much smaller than represented.' George, if this is correct, it's invaluable."

"I'd bank on it," George Crook said. "I know Miss Rebecca is devoted to the Union, and I'm certain the old Negro is reliable."

Phil put his feet over the side of the bed. "I'm delighted that it's true we outnumber Early."

The next day was one of the most exciting in Phil's life, for General Grant put Phil's army in motion with the terse words, "Go in."

Phil hastily assembled his generals. "I called you together," he said, "for a last word. On this map, prepared by Mr. Meigs, is the situation as I know it. This is an all or nothing campaign." Phil looked at the group of earnest officers. You could feel the friendliness and the pressure.

"Our chief scout, Major Young," Phil said, "reports that Early's army is on the high ground, two miles east of Winchester. He has cavalry on both ends of his line. The morale of the Confederates is not high. Lots of our spies report that. Our Major Young lays it to the way the war's been running and to Early's bitter, nasty disposition. Young certifies that Early's force is not a man over thirteen thousand."

The room was deathly quiet. Young Custer, in his gaudy uniform, stood next to the elderly General Emory.

Phil continued, "We have forty thousand, but it will take bravery and everything we've got to win. Tell your men, 'No surrender unless you are wounded and are out

of ammunition.' You will receive a detailed battle plan
later. We must win. I will accept nothing less than victory.
God bless you."

Near the town of Winchester the battle began. Phil's
cavalry rode toward a wooded ridge and struck the enemy.
The Confederates, in a strong position used two years
before by Stonewall Jackson, blasted Phil's cavalry, and
the horse-soldiers reeled backward.

Phil was on fire. He galloped Rienzi about the battlefield; he straightened out a traffic jam back on the Berryville Road.

He saw the problem. His army was not together. To
attack now would be taking a chance. If he waited until
everyone was in place, victory would be certain, but then
General Early would shift his reserve to meet the main
thrust, and casualties would be higher. Phil believed he
could win, and he wanted to win fast. He took a chance
and ordered a piecemeal attack. The part of Phil's line
that was ready marched forward. George Crook was
unhappy. He was not certain Phil was making the right
decision.

The very underbrush seemed to be trying to stop the
Union infantrymen. Shot, shell, and canister tore at them.
Union horse-drawn artillery dashed into position, unlimbered and went into action to help the infantry. The
ravine and the woods softened the roar of the cannons.
The explosions sounded hollow. Rifle fire sounded like
firecrackers. The drums were muted, as though the drum-
heads were wet. But the screams of the wounded were not
softened.

General Crook sent some of his men forward through a swamp, and numbers of them drowned. On his own, Crook ordered other parts of his corps around the left of the Confederate line, striking from the rear. The fighting was confused. Each man seemed to be fighting on his own.

Suddenly, the Confederates broke. They streamed south down the Pike toward Fisher's Hill. Their flight was a panic. The fierce Confederate, Jubal Early, swinging his sword, looked like a leader from the Old Testament as he stood in the smoke beside a red battle flag, trying to stem the flight.

The Union soldiers gave a great "Rebel Yell" of their own. George Crook was especially happy. He and his men had played a big part in gaining victory for Phil.

Phil rode up and congratulated Crook. "Let's go meet that Quaker schoolmarm," Phil said.

Together, they rode through the narrow streets of Winchester. In the schoolroom, the two generals thanked the handsome teacher for her part. Crook looked as though he had been in a coal mine. Black powder coated his side whiskers. A sooty streak emphasized his rugged nose.

Phil sat down at Rebecca Wright's desk and wrote a dispatch to President Lincoln. The teacher stood by, happy that she had helped the cause in which she believed.

In a few hours a reply came to Phil's telegram:

HAVE JUST HEARD OF YOUR GREAT VICTORY. GOD BLESS YOU ALL, OFFICERS AND MEN. STRONGLY INCLINED TO COME UP AND SEE YOU.

A. LINCOLN

Phil asked his adjutant general to copy the dispatch and to circulate it among his soldiers. It was great to be appreciated, especially by the President.

Phil relaxed. He believed all he had to do was to chase General Early up the Valley, but Colonel John Mosby stung Phil's army and disappeared.

On the Berryville Road, the daring Confederate raider attacked Phil's wagon trains. He ran off the train guards, captured two hundred of them, and destroyed seventy-five heavily loaded supply wagons. Then Mosby disappeared with two hundred beef cattle and five hundred and fifty spare horses and mules.

When Phil heard of this raid he exploded. His temper flared. He snapped at an aide, "Get me General Merritt."

When young Brigadier General Wesley Merritt, hard-riding cavalryman from Illinois, stood in front of him, Phil ranted, "I want you to catch that bushwhacker Mosby. Dead or alive. You understand, Merritt? Bring him in here."

But the Ranger, his men, and the captured Union soldiers, horses, and mules, vanished as if by magic. Merritt was a good Civil War cavalryman, but he could not solve mystery.

Now the part of the Shenandoah Phil had conquered burst into flame. At Phil's orders, barns, mills, and homes of people who were known to be Confederate sympathizers were set on fire. Smoke from the fires drifted across the floor of the Valley and hung in the tops of the Blue Ridge.

When Phil walked Rienzi down a road he saw looks of bewilderment on some of his artillerymen as they watched Union infantry set fire to a barn, haystacks, corn in the shock, and take cows and pigs from a farmer. "War's a terrible thing," Phil said to the artillerymen. "This is the only way we can end the threat from the Valley." He pointed to an ambulance back down the road loading wounded. "Remember, it's either us or them."

When Phil rode up on a knoll to the four tents serving as his headquarters, an adjutant general pointed at four men carrying a stretcher. The object on the litter was covered with a blanket. "Sir, bad news. Very, very bad news," the adjutant general said. "I feel terrible."

"Who is it?" Phil asked.

"Young Mr. John Meigs. He was murdered."

"Murdered?"

"Yes, sir. About a half-mile from here. Behind our lines. Meigs was walking along with his engineer sergeant when they met three men dressed in our uniform. Meigs spoke pleasantly to them. They passed, then turned and shot Mr. Meigs in the back. They were spies. The sergeant escaped. He said the three men ran toward the enemy lines after they shot the lieutenant."

Phil lifted the blanket covering John Meigs. The young second lieutenant looked almost as he had when he gave Phil the map report, only paler. The shock of brown hair still graced his forehead. Phil recoiled. He walked to the top of the hill and sat down on a log. The sun had gone. The Shenandoah Mountains to the west were shrouded in a purple haze. The Valley stretched south beneath him. He did not see its beauty. He thought only of Early, Mosby, their Confederates, and the murdered boy. "Get me General Custer," Phil shouted to an orderly.

Custer rode up, made his horse prance on two legs,

then vaulted to the ground and saluted almost in one motion. The events of the day made him look even fresher. His latest wrinkle was a three-inch silver star on the front slope of his forage cap. "General Custer reports to General Sheridan as ordered, sir," he said.

"Did you hear about Meigs?"

"Yes, sir." Custer's stringlike moustache did not hide his thin lips.

Phil stood up. He leveled his finger. "Custer, I am 'specially selecting you. I want you and your men to burn every home within five miles of here. I don't care who lives in them. And tell them why—John Meigs. Start at daybreak. I want it done fast," Phil concluded. "All delays are dangerous."

CHAPTER 20

Phil Sheridan at Cedar Creek

W HEN the buglers sounded the crisp notes of reveille, Phil's soldiers dragged themselves from their blankets and made their horseshoe-shaped rolls. It was dark, and the grass was wet with dew. The stars were still out. Small fires dotted the landscape. The advance guard, most of it cavalry, clattered out of camp, and their hoof-beats echoed down the road. Phil trotted Rienzi through camp while his men nibbled at hardtack and bacon and gulped coffee from their tin cups. "Today is the day we end our problems," he told them. "Early's men are eight miles south."

After breakfast, company officers checked their sleepy soldiers to make sure no one left his weapon or ammunition. When Phil gave the order, the columns formed in the fields and in the road. The march began. The smoldering campfires marked a step in Phil Sheridan's campaign against the daring Confederate, General Jubal Early.

Phil and his staff loped ahead to join the main part of the advance guard. The sun, now about to peep over the Blue Ridge, lined the crests with gold. The rays caught the smoke pouring upward from barns and mills. The bronzelike puffs were signs that the work of destruction was continuing. Phil gritted his teeth. The hard part of the job lay ahead: defeat of Early's army. He remembered Grant's warning—it would be a mistake to underestimate Early.

At noon rifle fire cracked out from the point of the advance guard. The Union army stopped. A cannon sounded its deep-throated *boom*. Phil had to restrain himself from going up to the point. He was anxious to start the battle and win. It seemed like an hour until a messenger galloped back to him reporting, "Sir, enemy pickets blocking the road."

"How many?" Phil demanded.

"Just a few, sir, but they got a cannon. The point's getting 'em out."

Massanutten Mountain loomed ahead. *What was it Mr. Meigs had to say about it?*

When stronger resistance halted the advance, Phil rode up a hill with his staff and his generals to look at the land over which they would battle. He felt like a boxer in a championship fight who has his opponent groggy and on the ropes. Phil was confident, determined to win.

The scout, Major Young, rode alongside him. Over his Confederate uniform Young wore a Union Army jacket for protection. When they were on the top of the hill Phil reined Rienzi. "Go ahead, Major," he said, "give your report."

Young's face tightened. He was not much older than Phil. "Yes, sir." Major Young pointed. "That's Fisher's

Hill. That's where his lines are, a mite over two miles long. Watch close and you might see one. They worked all night to dig those breastworks."

Phil focused his field glasses on Fisher's Hill. He saw only a red scar cut along the face of the hill below the crest.

"I've been over there," Young said. "General Early has a problem. His tongue is sharper than a razor, and his men say he is meaner than a bear in the spring. That and poor rations make him lose about fifty men a night by desertion."

"That's fine," Phil said. "Excuse me—go ahead."

Young continued. "Up on Massanutten Mountain— sir, that's that big hunk of rock covered with trees—they got a signal station. They see us right now and they can look down the throat of anything in this valley. That's all I have to say, General Sheridan, except some of our scouts are still over there. I hope they won't get hurt."

Phil reached over Rienzi's neck and shook the spy's hand. "Very good," Phil said. "Thank you."

The generals studied the situation. Finally Phil said, "What we'll do is smash straight into them. General Crook, you take your men around to the east and hit them from the flank."

Crook looked unhappy. He rubbed his large nose. "I wish you would change that, Ph—er, ah—General. Let me take my corps around their west flank. If we do that we'll be completely out of sight of their signal station and we might surprise them."

Phil changed his mind and agreed with George Crook. Phil turned to Brigadier General Averell, Indian-fighting cavalryman of the Regular Army. "Bill," Phil said, "when we knock the Confederates off that hill, I want you and your cavalry ready to gobble them up."

Averell wiped the lens of his field glasses with a bandanna. He was not much taller than Phil. When he talked his goatee moved up and down. "We'll be ready," he said confidently.

The afternoon dragged, except for an artillery duel and skirmishing by infantry. It seemed to Phil that Crook and his men would never get into position where they could strike. At suppertime the Confederates cooked their meal in the breastworks. You could see thin blue smoke, and every once in a while a spear of flame.

Suddenly there were yells. George Crook and his men burst down the mountainside and into the flank of the Confederate position. The entire Union line charged forward to help.

Early's men, badly surprised, gave ground, then tore for the rear.

When Phil saw that the battle was won he trotted to find Averell, his cavalry commander. When he found him, General Averell's horsemen were stringing picket lines so they could tie up their horses for the night. Some men were putting up tents. Phil forgot about the good work. He wanted perfection. He flew into a rage.

"Averell!" Phil bit off the words. "What are you doing? Why aren't you after the enemy?"

"We are blocked, sir. By our infantry."

"That's a measly, lame excuse. Why did you let them get ahead of you? You were to cut off the escape."

Before Averell could answer, Phil said, "This is the same

rotten leadership you showed a month ago in a skirmish near Harper's Ferry. You were drunk then, I hear."

General Averell's small face reddened. His goatee stuck straight out. "You cannot prove that," he said.

"You are relieved of your command," Phil said. "I want a leader." To an aide Phil said, "Tell the adjutant general about this and have him publish an order putting the cavalry under Colonel Powell."

"What do you want me to do?" Averell faltered.

"Nothing. I don't care what you do," Phil answered. "Go back to Harper's Ferry and take a rest. That's all you are interested in."

Major Young rode up. It was dusk. Phil could not make out his face very well, but the spy's happiness told in his voice. "Sir, I'd like permission to bring my men back for a rest. The Confederate Army is busted up. Jubal Early doesn't have an army any more."

"Yes, bring 'em in," Phil said, "and congratulate them for me. I'm proud of you all. I am recommending you for promotion."

When news of Phil's victories flashed through other Union armies, salutes of one hundred guns thundered in celebration. General Sherman's victory in the Battle of Atlanta and Phil's two victories made President Lincoln's election at the polls a certainty. Sheridan was riding on air.

But a problem developed. His long-time friend George Crook became angry. General Crook felt that neither he nor his men were given credit for their parts in the battles. And he had another protest. "You've removed the cavalry pickets at the fords along Cedar Creek," General Crook said.

"That puts my camp in danger." Crook looked extremely unhappy.

Phil sidestepped the complaint about not giving George Crook and his men credit for their hard fighting by saying, "There's credit enough for everyone. But about the pickets at the fords, you ought to know I need all the cavalry I can get to carry out my orders to burn up this Valley and to patrol after that Mosby."

"You're taking a chance," the grizzled brigadier general said, "and it is not a smart one. If Early counterattacks, he'll come through those fords. My camp is the farthest out and we'll be hit first. The fords are too far away to put infantry there."

"You have to take chances in war," Phil said, "and I'll take 'em."

"Supposing Early comes back? How about it?"

"I saw his retreat," Phil countered. "There's no Confederate army in the Valley. I don't want to hear anything more about it."

George Crook stalked off. Coolness developed between the two friends.

In a few weeks, Phil received a telegram from the Secretary of War to come to Washington for a conference on strategy. Phil ranted about being taken away from his army, but secretly he was pleased. He was delighted to be in on the big plans of the war, and he felt the order impressed his generals.

He pulled on his best uniform, stuck a new pair of buckskin gloves near the gold buckle of his sword belt, and mounted Rienzi. The big black was in tiptop condition. His saddle was polished. A new saddle blanket, with the coat of arms of the United States and two gold stars in each rear corner, graced his back. An escort of three hundred cavalrymen saluted Phil. They would guard him on the twenty-six mile ride to Martinsburg, where he would catch a train for Washington. Phil was taking no chances on being captured by Mosby.

On the road to Martinsburg, the desolation almost made Phil feel sorry for the Confederates. Farms and mills were wrecked. When he came to the ten-mile circle surrounding the spot where Lieutenant Meigs had been killed, there was nothing to mark the sites of homes but charred timbers. To the west, where his cavalry was still working, smoke draped a low-hanging cloud in black. Makeshift graves lined the roadside—Confederate and Union alike. The awfulness of war weighted him.

But far up the Valley the Confederate leader with the Biblical name had not given up. Jubal Early was not a quitter. General Lee sent him three thousand reinforcements. "Old Jube," as his men called him sometimes, worked his cavalry long hours to bring back every possible man. When his soldiers were divided into units, General Early decided to attack. He was a gambler facing long odds. He had thirteen thousand against Phil's forty thousand. Jubal Early told his generals and senior officers, "Just one victory will put things right." Early's whiskers seemed almost as if they were bristling. He despised Phil and his army.

Early's plan matched his boldness. The fierce Confederate explained it to his senior officer, John B. Gordon, a soldier's general. Gordon, lean hard fighter from Georgia, had risen from captain to two-star rank. He still had the drive he had at the beginning of the war, when he demanded that his company of Raccoon Roughs be allowed to fight for the Confederacy.

Jubal looked as fierce as his reputation, as he and John Gordon led their army through the unguarded fords on Cedar Creek. And just before sunrise they smashed through the sentinels guarding George Crook's bivouac. It was a foggy morning and the Confederates in their gray uniforms looked like ghosts as they bayoneted sentinels and shot up the camp.

The confusion was unbelievable. The Union army did not expect to fight, and their leader, Phil Sheridan, was in Washington.

Jubal Early's field pieces bellowed at the Union artillery positions on the high ground. Bluecoated officers shouted. They tried to form their men. Some Union soldiers ran around like recruits. Some obeyed orders. Others ran away. Union buglers and drummers sounded "Call to Arms," and were shot down. The scene was indescribable.

Phil Sheridan, on his way back to his army from the conference, was at Winchester when he first head the cannons. The noise came from the direction of his camp near Cedar Creek. He gulped his breakfast and ordered his three hundred cavalrymen to saddle up.

The noise of the battle became louder. Fourteen miles separated Phil from his men. A gust of yellow elm leaves blew in his face as he mounted Rienzi. He was nervous. He cursed the Secretary of War under his breath for taking him away from his army. Phil thought of George Crook's warning about removing the pickets guarding the fords. Phil hoped the enemy had not come through them.

After trotting an hour toward the battle, Phil shouted to

the horsemen riding behind him, "Halt! Dismount! Lead out!" He and his escorts swung out of the saddle and walked rapidly down the road, leading their mounts. The battle noises became louder.

A chaplain on a foam-covered horse galloped by. He waved his arm toward the battle and shouted at Phil, "All is lost, but it will be all right when you get there!"

In ten minutes Phil and his escort were back in the saddles, loping toward the danger. Bullets and shells whizzed overhead. A trooper near Phil went down. The road became clogged with wounded, men running to safety, wagon trains, and ambulances. Phil screamed at the stragglers to go back, but they paid no attention.

In order to go faster, Phil jumped Rienzi over a fence and galloped in the open fields.

When Phil and his escort trotted up a knoll, the battle was spread out beneath them. The Army of the Shenandoah was in an irregular line. It was barely holding its own. Some Confederates were looting a wagon train.

Phil snatched his red and white guidon with its two stars from an orderly. Rienzi was breathing hard, but Phil believed the horse was equal to another half mile of racing. He clamped his spurs to the animal's flanks and leaned low over his neck. The guidon whipped in the breeze. His escort could not keep up with Rienzi.

When Phil galloped onto the battlefield, he sat up, waved the pennant, and screamed. The Union soldiers cheered.

"Come with me, boys!" Phil shouted.

The Union lines straightened. The Bluecoats began to fire faster.

Phil tore for a Union regiment whose battle line was in a poor position. "Bring your Colors forward! Get on line!" he commanded.

A cavalry officer cried at Phil, "My God! I'm glad you've come!"

Union soldiers who were about to flee turned and joined their units. Phil encouraged them. The fighting was fierce; the two armies were at close range. The fight lasted six more hours. Finally, Phil's leadership and the weight of numbers won. Jubal Early was beaten for all time.

News of Phil's leadership in the crisis at Cedar Creek swept the North. Thomas B. Read wrote a poem glorifying Rienzi and Phil, and schoolboys learned it by heart. "Sheridan's Ride" was set to music and the picture on the sheet music showed Rienzi carrying Phil through smoke.

In his own handwriting, President Lincoln thanked Phil for his fighting in the Shenandoah and for his leadership at Cedar Creek.

Phil did not talk of Crook's warning about the unguarded fords, but Crook wrote of it years later.

Operations in the Valley now slowed. There was one splinter in Phil's contentment: Colonel John S. Mosby. Phil spread nets of cavalry to catch the Ranger, but Mosby was not to be caught. Instead, Mosby captured General George Crook in a hotel and sent him to Richmond as a prisoner.

With the great Shenandoah Valley black, barren, and cheerless, Phil marched his army back to General Grant. One problem remained and that was a big one: how to defeat the soldier whose leadership was keeping the Confederates fighting, General Robert E. Lee.

CHAPTER 21

Phil Helps to End the War

WHEN Phil reported to Grant at City Point, six miles northeast of Petersburg on the James River, Phil was amused. He expected General Grant to make a show over the campaign in the Shenandoah. Instead, when Phil walked into Grant's tent the general-in-chief merely removed his cigar, made a pretext of returning Phil's salute, and smiled slightly. Grant said flatly, "How are you?"

There was nothing showy about U. S. Grant. He had no time to waste, but neither was he hasty. The wind whipping his tent seemed in far more of a hurry than Grant.

The general-in-chief's brown beard tilted downward as he motioned Phil to a map spread on a rough-hewn table. "Take a look," Grant said.

The tent was new, and Phil liked the peculiar smell of the canvas. He felt happy. He was buoyed by General Grant's matter-of-fact confidence as Grant said, "We do not want to butt our heads any more against Lee's trenches. I'm going to force him out of those trenches and forts, and away from those land torpedoes and trip irons, those deadly wires men trip over and explode nearby shells."

Grant dropped his stubby cigar and stepped on it. "When we get Lee out I'm going to hang on to him like a bulldog. We've enough men here now to finish the job. Lee's pressed for 'em." Grant placed a finger on Petersburg. "When I give the word, Sheridan, I want you to ride south of the city and swing out and capture Five Forks. This is an important road junction nearabout thirteen miles southwest of town. You get in Lee's rear. He'll be forced to stretch his lines and fight us in the open. When he does that we have him. We'll cut up his army and the war will end."

Phil was thrilled. This was his style: a series of blows and no letup. Grant was not going by rules. He was not concerned with capturing cities. Lee's army was the target.

Grant took a cigar from a box on the table. "When will your men be ready?" he said.

"Give me a week, General. Almost every horse we have needs shoeing."

Grant went over his plan again. He stressed the importance of Five Forks. "You control that place out there on the flank of Lee's line and he'll have to come out and fight. What do you think?"

Grant's businesslike attitude and his quiet enthusiasm made Phil want to fight now. He forgot that his horses needed shoes. He banged the table. "Let me go now, sir. I can do the job."

General Grant folded the map and placed it carefully in his dispatch case. He knew the magnetic power Phil held over men in a fight, and he sensed a lack of this power in himself. He also knew Phil was impatient.

"Glad you feel that way," Grant said. "We'll go soon

enough, but all of us have work to do to get ready. Get your hat. I want to take you to see the President."

When General Grant and Phil boarded the river steamer *Mary Martin*, they found Abraham Lincoln leaning over the rail watching Phil's horsemen cross a canal on a pontoon bridge. Abe Lincoln answered the cheers of the cavalrymen by raising his tall black hat and smiling. But when he sat inside the cabin with the two generals his mood changed. He looked worn and tired. His shoulders sagged. The strain had aged him greatly since Phil first met him six months ago.

Lincoln stretched his long legs and clasped his hands behind his head. "Sheridan," he said, "you've changed my ideas of what a cavalryman should be. I used to think a horse soldier should be at least six feet tall. You'll do in a pinch."

Phil grinned. He twisted an end of his moustache and kept still.

"I saw your report from the Shenandoah," the President said. "If I recall, you burned over a thousand barns and— ah, how many mills?"

"Seventy-one, sir," Phil said.

"And if I recall some more, you captured over twenty-five hundred horses and approximately a thousand beef cattle. How much wheat?"

"We destroyed about a half-million bushels, sir."

"Those were his orders," Grant said, as if Phil needed to be defended.

"And what else?" the President asked.

"We beat Early's army, sir."

"Some of Early's men joined Lee," Grant said.

"Suppose the enemy came down here to City Point and captured this supply area?" the President said. He was not cheerful.

Phil answered quickly while Grant studied the question. "That's impossible, sir. Lee has all he can do to hold his trenches around Petersburg and to defend Richmond."

The President looked at Grant. Grant replied, "That's correct. It's what I believe. We expect more raids against our steamboats by the Confederate Secret Service. That's why I have patrols and guards up and down this river, but Sheridan's right."

The President slouched in his seat as he studied the two generals. He reminded Phil of a sorrowful hound. He closed his eyes. Phil thought of all of Abe Lincoln's troubles: politics, generals who disappointed him, officers pressing to become generals, high prices, the cost of the war, obtaining men and still more men for battles.

Grant said, "Mr. President, I have a plan to end the war."

Lincoln sat bolt upright. His brow knitted.

"First, I want to say," Grant continued, "we managed to exchange General Crook. When we attack, he'll command a cavalry division."

"Good," Lincoln said.

General Grant spread out his map and went over his plan. When he finished, President Lincoln said, "I'm glad to get out of Washington and to hear this. It won't be easy, will it?"

"Lee's no fool," Grant said.

"I only hope things work your way," Mr. Lincoln said. "Afterward we face a bigger problem."

Phil started to say, "What is that?" but he kept still.
Lincoln added, "Getting the Union back together and
preserving it."

It was almost a month after the conference on the river
steamer when General Grant gave Phil his go-ahead orders.

Phil's cavalrymen swung into the saddle, ready to fight.
Equipment had been stripped down. Four days' rations
were in the saddlebags. The target was Five Forks. But,
somehow, Lee read Grant's mind. He ordered one of his
best fighters, General George Pickett, famous because of his
charge at Gettysburg, to go to Five Forks. And Pickett had
nineteen thousand men with him.

Before Phil's cavalrymen had ridden very far down the
muddy roads, Phil received word from Lieutenant Colonel
Young, his scout, that Pickett held Five Forks.

Phil called a halt. He assembled his young brigadiers
and his staff officers. They stood under a huge oak. Around
them cavalrymen lay on their backs holding the reins of
their mounts.

Phil said, "Gentlemen, I'm going to take a chance. My
orders are to go around and get behind Pickett, but if we
can shove a wedge between him and Lee's army, what will
Pickett do? Where will he be?" Phil answered his own
question. "He'll be in danger and we can trap him. Does
anyone disagree?"

Custer slapped his leg with his fringed gauntlets. He
looked at the orderly holding his horse. George Custer
wanted to go.

"All right." Phil beamed. "Let's lead out."

Someone said, "If these roads don't dry up how will we get forage for the horses?"

"Forage?" Phil shouted. "I'll get all the forage we want. If we have to I'll put every man to cutting trees and corduroying roads. I tell you, I am ready to strike out and go to smashing things."

But to trap Pickett Phil needed more men, and he needed them in a hurry. He knew that General Grant was sending Major General G. K. Warren to him with sixteen thousand soldiers.

There was no word from Warren.

Warren, the hero of Gettysburg, was having difficulties. A stream he had to cross was flooded and his men were delayed. Phil sent a string of staff officers to Warren. The message was: *Hurry. We can trap Pickett at Five Forks.*

Finally, Phil could wait no longer. He started the fight without Warren. He sent Colonel Mackenzie, the hardbitten young fighter, as sharp a knife as Custer, with cavalry to circle from the west and slash at Pickett's men.

Soon Phil worried. He was afraid his horsemen would run out of ammunition. He was impatient—so angry that no one approached him. He set out himself to hurry Warren to the battle.

When Phil found General Warren, Phil was like a caged tiger. Warren was tired but cool. His matter-of-fact attitude irritated Phil. Warren rubbed his big nose and listened to Phil's plan. Warren was not "on fire," like the young generals Phil was used to. To Phil, General Warren seemed placid, unenthusiastic about the plan to attack.

A Union cavalry band in the distance, under enemy fire,

was playing "Nellie Bly." *At least,* Phil thought, *they are doing more than Warren's men.*

When Phil's staff officers finally placed Warren's soldiers in the battle line, they made a mistake. Yet when Warren's line went forward through the woods, he and his infantry-men swung around and hit Pickett's flank and rear correctly.

At the same time, Phil hurled men at Pickett's front. Mackenzie, Sheridan, and Warren had Pickett and his men in a fiery set of tongs.

During the battle, Phil and Custer took chances to en-courage the men. The whine of bullets did not bother them. Custer, yellow curls and red necktie flying, seemed to be daring enemy sharpshooters to hit him. Phil screamed for his red and white headquarters' flag. He cursed, then lifted the guidon over his head and cried, "Oh, God, who art the author of peace and lover of concord!" He braced the staff of the flag between his leg and Rienzi's side. An orderly be-hind Phil fell out of his saddle, dead. A bullet grazed Phil's arm. Men about him fell. Phil pointed the tip of his guidon slightly toward the Confederates and led the charge. The sound of the bugles, the yells of the troopers, and the noise of firing were deafening.

Phil's men overwhelmed the enemy. They captured four thousand five hundred soldiers, six cannons, and thirteen battle flags.

Phil turned Rienzi after the battle and rode about the field to find Warren. When Phil found the New Yorker, Phil was still trembling from excitement. Because he felt that Warren did not inspire his men and did not control them, Phil relieved General Warren and took away his command. This started an argument that lasted for years.

Many believed that Phil acted unjustly, but later, when General Grant was asked about it, he said Phil was right in taking away Warren's command.

Exciting word came from Richmond, the Confederate capital. President Jefferson Davis ordered the removal of the Confederate treasury and its records. Richmond was abandoned, and a mob began looting. Fire spread. The Confederate capital was doomed.

General Lee was desperate. He and his army left the trenches and Petersburg and headed southwest toward Danville, Virginia; maybe they were going to South Carolina.

Phil's soldiers sensed the end of the war was near. They slashed at Lee and captured his rear guard and trains.

Lee's half-starved, exhausted army began to crumble.

When it was certain that further fighting was useless, General Lee sent a white linen dishcloth to General Grant as a sign of truce. The two leaders exchanged letters arranging for the surrender, and soon the senior officers gathered in the red-brick McLean farmhouse at Appomattox.

Not far away, George Custer galloped up to the grizzled Confederate, Lieutenant General Longstreet. Longstreet had graduated from West Point nineteen years before Custer. General Custer displayed the lack of modesty and the boldness which would cost lives at the Little Bighorn nine years later. "I want your instant surrender," he demanded of Longstreet.

The burly Confederate shouted at Custer, "General Lee is talking to General Grant. Now you go, or I'll teach you a lesson you will remember forever."

In the McLean house General Lee, wearing an immaculate full-dress uniform and a jeweled sword at his belt, waited for General Grant. Even Lee's spurs glistened. But his eyes, and the rings beneath them, told some of the story. The Confederate leader was worn out. For him the trail that started in 1861, when he resigned his Regular Army commission to fight for Virginia, had come to a bitter end. It was Palm Sunday, April 9, 1865.

General Grant, Phil, and other principal officers, walked into the room where General Lee and members of his staff waited. There was a conference in private between the two seniors.

Now the two generals sat at little tables not far apart and arranged surrender terms and signed them. Grant's private's uniform and his boots were spattered with mud. He wore no spurs. His three-star epaulets were tarnished. There were brief conversations in a strained atmosphere. Perhaps at first General Grant was embarrassed.

The terms Grant gave Lee were generous. The Confederates were to keep their swords and pistols, their horses and baggage, and were allowed to go home. They were not to become prisoners.

Phil stood silently beside the fireplace watching the simple ceremonies ending America's worst war. There was talk of rations, for Lee's army was starving. Grant said, "How many men do you have, General?"

"Indeed, I don't know," Lee replied. "The fighting. We have lost records."

Grant turned to Phil, because he had captured the Confederate wagon trains. "Sheridan," General Grant said, "suppose you send enough food to General Lee for twenty-five thousand men for one day."

"Yes, sir," Phil answered.

Robert E. Lee shook hands with U. S. Grant. Lee pocketed his steel-rimmed spectacles. He tugged on his gauntlets and left.

Outside, Lee mounted Traveller, the gray horse that had borne him through the campaigns, and rode away. His Army rushed to him, their hats off. They wanted him to talk. Lee stopped Traveller and said, "We have been through this together. My heart is too full to say more."

The Union Army began to cheer and to fire guns in celebration. "I want that stopped," Grant said to his staff. "There is no use rejoicing over a fallen enemy."

Phil purchased one of the two tables used at the surrender for Custer and his wife. Phil was happy the war was over. He wanted the Custers to have a valuable souvenir.

That night, in his tent, Phil opened the battered dispatch case he had captured at Booneville, Missouri, and took out pencil and paper so that he could write home. In the case he found a stained scrap of paper. It read: *No man is an island, no man stands alone—John Donne.*

Phil's brow wrinkled. "I don't know any 'John Donne,'" he said. Then he remembered that, in the moonlight on the top of Missionary Ridge, Jim Card had given him this quote before leaving for East Tennessee.

Phil thought of others who had helped him since the war began. General Halleck, who gave him his first chance. Captain Alger, the Wolverine, who led the surprise attack at Boonville. Captain Campbell, who gave him Rienzi. General Thomas, who saved the day at Chickamauga. The brigadier generals, his "young tigers," who helped defeat Jeb Stuart at Yellow Tavern, who fought in the Valley, and who worked so hard to help end the war at Five Forks.

Second Lieutenant John Meigs, whose maps assisted in the Shenandoah Valley, and who was killed in that campaign. General George Crook, a real fighter. Miss Rebecca Wright, the Quaker schoolteacher, and the Negro who carried the notes. Lieutenant Colonel H. K. Young, chief of scouts, and his brave volunteers, who operated behind the lines in Confederate uniforms. General Grant, the determined leader, who never made the same mistake twice, and who had the courage and brains to fight through to victory. U. S. Grant had given Phil his biggest opportunities.

Phil read again the message giving him the thanks of Congress: *To General Sheridan and the officers and men under his command, for the gallantry, military skill and courage displayed . . . in the valley of the Shenandoah, and especially for their services at Cedar Run. . . .*" His lively eyes reread the message. *The officers and soldiers.*

Many were in graves south of the Potomac. The services and sacrifices of his officers and men had enabled Phil Sheridan to help the United States.

FOR FURTHER READING

In writing this book my principal guideposts were:

Philip Henry Sheridan, *Personal Memoirs*, two volumes, Charles L. Webster Co., N. Y., 1888.

Richard O'Connor, *Sheridan The Inevitable*, The Bobbs-Merrill Co., Inc., N. Y., 1953.

Colonel Vincent J. Esposito, *The West Point Atlas of American Wars*, volume I, Frederick A. Praeger, N. Y., 1959.

Battles and Leaders of the Civil War, four volumes, The Century Co., N. Y., 1884–87.

Lieutenant Colonel Mark M. Boatner's *Civil War Dictionary*, published by David McKay Co., Inc., in 1959, was also extraordinarily helpful, and makes interesting reading.

SELECTED BOOKS

Among the books consulted, I also received special guidance from:

Agassiz, George R., *Meade's Headquarters, 1863–1865* (Letters of Colonel Theodore Lyman), The Atlantic Monthly Press, Boston, 1922.

Catton, Bruce, *A Stillness at Appomattox*, Doubleday & Co., Inc., N. Y., 1954.

Forman, Sidney, *West Point*, Columbia University Press, N. Y., 1952.

Freeman, Douglas Southall, *Lee's Lieutenants*, volume III, Charles Scribner's Sons, N. Y., 1944.

Grant, Ulysses Simpson, *Personal Memoirs*, volume II, Charles L. Webster Co., N. Y., 1885.

Herr, John K., Major General, and Wallace, Edward S., *The Story of the U. S. Cavalry, 1775–1924*, Little, Brown & Co., Boston, 1953.

Milhollen, H. D., Johnson, J. R., and Bill, A. H., *Horsemen Blue and Gray*, Oxford University Press, N. Y., 1960.

Sandburg, Carl, *Abraham Lincoln*, volume III, Harcourt, Brace & Co., 1939.

Schmitt, Martin F., *General George Crook, His Autobiography*, University of Oklahoma Press, Norman, Oklahoma, 1960.

Williams, T. Harry, *Lincoln and His Generals*, Grosset & Dunlap, N. Y., 1952.

Index

Adams, Sergeant, 98
Alger, Captain, 107, 110–11, 229
Antietam, Battle of, 124, 160
Appomattox, 227
Archer, Captain James, 98
Army of the Potomac, 164, 165, 168, 169, 174
Army of the Shenandoah, 195, 218
Arnold, Benedict, 38
Atlanta, 192–93, 214
Averell, Brigadier General Bill, 212–14

Beaver Dam Station, 180–81
Bedloe's Island, 72, 125
Blair, Governor, 106
Booneville, Mississippi, 107, 170, 229
Bowling Green, Kentucky, 125
Bragg, General Braxton, 114, 130, 137, 141, 143–44, 151, 154, 155, 161
Brewerton, Captain Henry, 22–23, 27, 34, 36, 37, 45–46, 79
Buckner, General Simon B., 118
Buell, General Don Carlos, 115–24, 195

Bull Run
  First Battle of, 99, 104, 160
  Second Battle of, 112, 160, 172
Butler, Benjamin (general and politician), 184

Camp La Pena, 63, 64
Campbell, Captain, 113–14, 170, 229
Card, Jim, 126–33, 137, 139, 143–53, 154, 158–59, 162–63, 192, 229
Cedar Creek, 214, 217–19, 230
Chalmers, General James R., 109, 120
Chambersburg, Pennsylvania, 193
Chancellorsville, 160
Chattanooga, 157, 160
Chickamauga, 156–57, 229
Civil War, 97–230
Cleveland, Ohio, 11–12
Clinton, Brigadier General James, 36
Cold Harbor, Battle of, 185, 186, 188–90
Constitution Island, 16, 17
"Cracker Line," 158, 159, 160
Crook, Major General George, 39, 42, 48, 50, 77, 82, 90–91,

94, 198, 200, 201, 203–6,
212–15, 217, 219, 223, 230
Curtis, Major General, 102–4
Custer, Major General George,
172, 176–77, 178, 180–83,
186, 187, 188, 192, 195,
204, 208–9, 224, 225, 226,
227, 229

Davis, Jefferson, 58, 99, 227
Davis, Matt, 22, 25, 26, 32, 44,
48
Doctor's Creek, 119–20

Early, Lieutenant General Jubal
A., 193, 194, 195, 198, 200–
1, 204–8, 210–19, 222
Emory, General William H., 197,
204
Erie Canal, 13

Fisher's Hill, 211–12
Five Forks, 221, 224, 225, 229
Forrest, General Nathan Bedford,
172
Fort Duncan (Texas), 50, 59–70
Fort Reading (California), 79–
80, 86
Fowler, Colonel, 62, 69, 78
Frankman, Private, 65–70
Fredericksburg, 160
Frémont, Major General John,
101–2

Garesché, Colonel, 135
Gates, General Horatio, 36
Gettysburg, 160, 169, 224, 225
Gordon, General John B., 216–
17

Governors Island, 72
Grant, General Ulysses S., 141,
159–63, 165, 167–71, 176,
177, 181, 185, 186, 189,
190–96, 204, 211, 219,
220–25, 228–29, 230
Greene, General Nathaniel, 36
Gregg, General Dave M., 186–87

Halleck, General Henry W., 100–
6, 112, 141, 165–68, 229
Hampton, General Wade, 188,
192
Harrington, Colonel, 135
Henry, Private Joseph, 85
Hood, John, 49, 77, 79, 81, 82,
85, 91–92, 153, 156, 158
Horseshoe Ridge, 157, 167
Hudson River, 14
Hunter, General David, 193

Indians, 51–52, 54, 63–69, 77,
79–80, 82, 85–92, 95–97,
99

Jackson, General Stonewall, 112,
156, 172, 194, 205
Jefferson, Thomas, 22
Jefferson Barracks (St. Louis), 99

Kelton, Colonel John, 105
Knox, General Henry, 36

Lafayette, Georgia, 151, 154
Lee, General Robert E., 112, 153,
169, 171, 172, 185, 189,
216, 219, 220–24, 227–29
Lincoln, President Abraham, 97,
99, 112, 126, 138, 141, 158,

160, 167–70, 190, 193, 195, 200, 206–7, 214, 219, 222–24

Longstreet, General James, 153, 156, 227

Lookout Mountain, 143, 154

Lyman, Ted (Volunteer *aide-de-camp* to General George Meade), 172, 187, 188

Mackenzie, Colonel Ranald, 176–77, 182, 195, 225, 226

Marion, General Francis, 36

Massanutten Mountain, 198, 211, 212

McClellan, General George B., 124, 190

McPherson, General James Birdseye, 49, 104, 179, 192–93

Meade, General George, 165, 169, 170–77, 181, 184–85, 187, 189

Meigs, Lieutenant John R., 197–98, 204, 208, 209, 211, 216, 230

Merritt, Brigadier General Wesley, 207

Missionary Ridge, 143, 154, 158–61, 166, 229

Morgan, General John Hunt, 172–73

Mosby, Colonel John (Confederate Ranger), 207, 208, 215, 216, 219

Moultrie, General William, 36

Nelson, General "Bull," 115

Nugent, John, 48

Oregon Territory, 69, 79–99

Perryville, Battle of, 122–24, 125

Pickett, Major General George, 224–26

Pierce, President Franklin, 58

Polk, President James, 3

Powell, Colonel, 214

Putnam, Colonel Israel, 36

Rains, Major Gabriel, 95–97

Read, Thomas B., 219

Resaca de la Palma, Battle of, 58

Richmond, Virginia, 182, 189, 227

Rienzi (Sheridan's horse), 113–15, 119, 120, 121, 122, 124, 125, 128, 134, 142, 147, 151, 155, 156, 159, 164, 165, 171, 178, 180, 205, 207, 210, 211, 212, 215, 217, 218, 219, 226, 229

Ritchey, Thomas, 6

Roberts, Colonel G. W., 128, 130, 135, 137

Rosecrans, General William S., 124, 125, 128–38, 140–42, 147, 149, 150, 154–60, 172, 195

Schaefer, Colonel Frederick, 128, 134

Schuyler, General Philip, 36

Scott, General Winfield, 3, 20, 28, 33–38, 97, 116

Shenandoah Valley, 192, 193, 194, 197–209, 230

Sheridan, Patrick, 5

Sheridan, General Philip Henry
Civil War and, 100–230
Fort Duncan days, 50–70
Oregon Territory days, 79–99
trip to Oregon Territory, 71–78
West Point days, 3–49, 50
"Sheridan's Ride," 219
Sherman, General William T., 170, 193, 214
Shiloh, Battle of, 105
Slocum, Major General Hank, 22–26, 32–33, 45, 46, 48, 104, 160
Smith, Kirby, 114
Somerset, Ohio, 4, 6, 47, 100
Spotsylvania Court House, 177, 178
Stanley, General Dave, 13–26, 31, 42, 44, 46, 48, 104
Stanton, Secretary of War Edwin, 167, 198
Stones River, Battle of, 125–39
Stuart, General James E. B., 49, 172, 176, 177, 179, 180, 182, 184, 188, 229

Taylor, President Zachary ("Old Rough and Ready"), 12
Terrill, Brigadier General William, 39–45, 48–49, 54, 120–21, 123, 136, 149
Texas, 51–70
Texas Rangers, 54, 69
Thayer, Colonel Sylvanus ("The Father of West Point"), 32
Thickstun, Captain, 158–59
Thomas, General George, 117, 136, 141, 147–49, 154–55, 157, 158, 164, 165, 166, 167, 169, 229
Traveller (Lee's horse), 229
Trevilian Station, 192
Trimble, Major, 118

Uncle Tom's Cabin, 56, 58
Underground Railroad, 11

VanBuren, Captain Michael, 63, 65
Vicksburg, 159, 170

Warren, Major General G. K., 175, 225–27
Washington, President George, 15, 16, 37
Wayne, General Anthony, 36
West Point, 4–49, 50, 54, 62, 94, 117
Wheeler, General ("Fightin' Joe"), 120, 133
White Oak Swamp, 169
Wilder, Colonel J. T., 117–18
Wilderness, the, 171, 173, 174
Wilkerson, Dan, 52–59
Williamson, Lieutenant R. S., 77, 81–93
Winchester, 206, 217
Wright, Rebecca, 200, 204, 206, 230

Yellow Tavern, 182, 229

Young, H. K., 202, 203, 204, 211–12, 214, 230